Strategies
of Genius

Volume II

Albert Einstein

by

Robert B. Dilts

Meta Publications
P.O. Box 1910
Capitola, California 95010
(408) 464 - 0254
FAX (408) 464 - 0517

Original artwork by Robert B. Dilts.

Library of Congress Card Number 94-77-813
I.S.B.N. 0-916990-33-8

Contents

Dedication   v
Acknowledgments   vii
Preface   ix

INTRODUCTION   xi
  Levels of Modeling   xiv
  Strategies   xvi
  Micro, Macro and Meta Strategies   xvii

CHAPTER 1 EINSTEIN'S EPISTEMOLOGY   1
  Footnotes to Chapter 1   25

CHAPTER 2 EINSTEIN'S MACRO-STRATEGY
FOR MODELING   27
Challenging Basic Assumptions   28
Footnotes to Chapter 2   42

CHAPTER 3 THE BASIC STRUCTURE OF
EINSTEIN'S THINKING STRATEGY   45
Footnotes to Chapter 3   55

CHAPTER 4 EINSTEIN'S VIEW OF LANGUAGE   57
Footnotes to Chapter 4   69

CHAPTER 5 MICRO-ANALYSIS OF EINSTEIN'S
CREATIVE THINKING PROCESS   71
Footnotes to Chapter 5   84

CHAPTER 6 THE THEORY OF RELATIVITY   85
Challenging Basic Assumptions About 'Space'   90
Challenging Basic Assumptions
    About 'Simultaneity'   96
Challenging Basic Assumptions About 'Time'   104
Some Implications of Einstein's
    Theory of Relativity   112
Footnotes to Chapter 6   132

CHAPTER 7 SOME PSYCHOLOGICAL
IMPLICATIONS OF THE THEORY OF RELATIVITY   133
Footnotes to Chapter 7   154

CHAPTER 8 APPLICATIONS OF EINSTEIN'S
THEORY OF RELATIVITY   155
Seeing New Levels and Dimensions   157
Using Symbolic Metaphors to Find and
    Challenge Basic Assumptions   161
A Format For Resolving Conflicts Based on
    Einstein's Strategy   171
A Strategy for 'Mediation' Based on
    Einstein's Thinking Process   176
Footnotes to Chapter 8   178

CHAPTER 9 SUMMARY OF EINSTEIN'S
THINKING PROCESS   179

CHAPTER 10 CONCLUSION   185
Footnotes to Chapter 10   200

AFTERWORD   201

APPENDIX A PRINCIPLES OF NLP   203

APPENDIX B PRESUPPOSITIONS OF NLP   221

APPENDIX C GLOSSARY OF NLP TERMINOLOGY   225

BIBLIOGRAPHY   233

Dedication

This book is dedicated with love and respect to
Gino Bonissone
who has the mind of an Einstein
and the heart of an Italian.

Acknowledgments

I would like to acknowledge:

My wife Anita, and my children Andrew and Julia whose understanding, patience and support made it possible for me to put in the extra effort necessary to complete this book;

Todd Epstein who helped me to develop the "laboratory" for my "thought experiments";

Michael Pollard and Ami Sattinger who "went the extra mile" with me to finish this volume;

And all those who have kept the spirit of Albert Einstein alive and burning bright.

Preface

In my preface to the first volume of this series on *Strategies of Genius* I pointed out that this work is the fulfillment of a vision that began almost twenty years ago. In a class at the University of California at Santa Cruz, called *Pragmatics of Human Communication,* I had a conversation with John Grinder about the possibility of mapping the sequences in which exceptional people unconsciously employed their senses while they were thinking. I was at that time a junior in college and John Grinder was a professor of linguistics.

The discussion planted a seed in me about a larger study of the cognitive patterns of well known geniuses, that would on the one hand honor their brilliance, and at the same time demystify it and make it have more practical applications. Part of the idea was that these strategies could be coded into basic yet simple enough terms that aspects of them could even be taught to children in preparation for challenges they would face in their adult lives. That seed eventually grew into this series of books.

In *Volume I* explored the creative processes of Aristotle, Arthur Conan Doyle's Sherlock Holmes, Walt Disney and Wolfgang Amadeus Mozart. Future volumes will include studies of Leonardo da Vinci, Sigmund Freud, John Stewart Mill, Nicola Tesla and some more recent 'geniuses' such as Gregory Bateson, Moshe Feldenkrais and Milton H. Erickson, M.D.

This volume is devoted entirely to Albert Einstein. The purpose of the book is to analyze the thinking processes at the basis of Einstein's unique personality and accomplishments. Using the cognitive modeling techniques of Neuro-Linguistic Programming, I will explore some of the essential elements of Einstein's mental strategies and beliefs and hopefully make them more "user friendly."

The intention of the study is to look beyond the specific content and scientific details of Einstein's thoughts to the cognitive 'strategies of genius' that created them. NLP provides a structure and a language to be able to put Einstein's mental processes into a usable set of 'chunks' or steps that can be applied to everyday life.

By examining numerous quotations, excerpts from Einstein's own writings and anecdotes, I intend to paint a rich picture of Einstein's thinking processes and demonstrate how his strategies may be used by the reader to enhance his or her own creativity and problem solving ability.

Many of Einstein's "thought experiments" and the descriptions of his thinking strategies are entertaining and surprisingly simple. Some chapters, however, may be challenging to some readers. The implications of some of Einstein's ideas can be overwhelming in themselves. While readers can always skip ahead and return later, any effort invested in getting through difficult areas will be well rewarded. In fact, I recommend that you read some of the chapters, such as the one on relativity, twice - just to give it time to 'sink in'.

It may also help to keep in mind that this book is not intended to simply be a 'biography'. In fact, in many ways it is more of a 'work book'. My goal is to take the reader inside the mind of Einstein and begin to view reality as he would. I think you will find it to be a remarkable journey.

Introduction

*"...the essential in the being of a man of my type lies precisely in what he thinks and **how** he thinks, not in what he does or suffers."* [1] - ***Albert Einstein***

Albert Einstein (1879-1955) is not only acknowledged around the world as a genius but has practically become the symbol for genius in this century. The problem space that his ideas dealt with encompasses our spiritual and social worlds as well as scientific and physical reality. He introduced a whole new paradigm of thinking that has affected many different areas of our lives.

His discoveries in the field of theoretical physics made the "atomic age" possible and his humanitarianism has served as an example for all of science. His theory of relativity changed our entire conception of the universe and such basic aspects of our reality as time, space, matter and energy. Einstein's way of thinking allowed him to construct new models of reality as well as creatively challenge basic presuppositions in the existing models of his time.

How do we make sense out of a man like Einstein? What can we learn from him? Was his genius a function of his genetics? divine inspiration? a lucky accident? or perhaps a specific thinking process that might be possible to teach to others? Einstein himself posed similar questions about the great Isaac Newton (creator of differential calculus, the laws of gravitation and motion, and the father of modern physics) when he wrote:

> *"Newton was the first to succeed in finding a clearly formulated basis from which he could deduce a wide field of phenomena by means of mathematical thinking, logically, quantitatively and in harmony with experience...*

"How did this miracle come to birth in his brain? For if by reason we could deal with the problem of the 'how,' then there could be no question of a miracle in the proper sense of the word. It is the goal of every activity of the intellect to convert a 'miracle' into something which may be grasped. If in this case the miracle permits itself to be converted, our admiration for the mind of Newton becomes only greater thereby." [2]

This is precisely the issue I seek to address with Einstein - to tackle the "problem of the 'how'" in relationship to Einstein himself. How did Einstein's own incredible ideas "come to birth in his brain?" How can we to some extent demystify the "miracle" of Einstein's mental abilities and convert them into something which may be "grasped" by our intellects in such a way that our admiration for his mind becomes that much greater?

Neuro-Linguistic Programming (NLP) provides a new set of tools that can allow us to take major steps toward this promising but elusive goal. The mission of NLP has been to define and extend the leading edge of human knowledge - especially our knowledge about ourselves. This work on Einstein, the second volume of a larger study on the *Strategies of Genius*, is a part of that mission. My goal is to model the thinking strategies of people who have not only contributed to our knowledge of the world around us, but have also contributed to our knowledge about ourselves. It is my hope that we can discover how to use those strategies to further contribute to the evolution of our species and our planet.

One of the great contributions of NLP is that it gives us a way to look past the behavioral content of what people do to the more invisible forces behind those behaviors; to the structures of thought that has allowed these geniuses to accomplish what they accomplished. NLP provides a structure and a language to be able to put into a set of chunks or steps the relevant mental processes used by a Mozart,

Leonardo or Einstein so that those mental processes can be transferred to others.

The other tremendous contribution of NLP is that by looking at the underlying structure of an activity it allows us to transcend the content of that activity to the degree that we can apply the thinking process of genius in one field to another entire area of content. We can discover certain key elements of how Einstein thought about physics and apply them to thinking about social organization, effective business practice, managerial issues or resolving personal problems.

Levels of Modeling

In modeling an individual there are a number of different aspects, or levels, of the various systems and sub-systems in which that person operated that we may explore. For instance, we can look at the historical and geographical *environment* in which Einstein lived - i.e., *when* and *where* he operated. We can examine an individual's specific *behaviors* and actions - i.e., *what* Einstein did in that environment. We may also look at the intellectual and cognitive strategies and *capabilities* by which Einstein selected and guided his actions in the environment - i.e., *how* he generated these behaviors in that context. We could further explore the beliefs and values that motivated and shaped the thinking strategies and capabilities that the individual developed to accomplish his or her behavioral goals in the environment - i.e., *why* Einstein did things the way he did them in those times and places. And we could look even deeper in order to investigate the individual's perception of the self or identity he or she was manifesting through that set of beliefs, capabilities and actions in that environment - i.e., the *who* behind the why, how, what, where and when.

We might also want to examine the way in which that identity manifested itself in relationship to the individual's family, colleagues, contemporaries, Western Society and Culture, the planet, God - i.e., who Einstein was in relation to *who else*. In other words, how did Einstein's behaviors, abilities, beliefs, values and identity influence and interact with larger systems of which he was a part in a personal, social and ultimately *spiritual* way?

In summary, modeling the process of genius may involve exploring the interactions of a number of different levels of experience, including:

Spiritual	Vision & Purpose
A. *Who I Am* - Identity	Mission
B. *My Belief System* -	Values, Meta Programs
	Permission & Motivation
C. *My Capabilities* -	States, Strategies
	Direction
D. *What I Do* -	Specific Behaviors
	Actions
E. *My Environment* -	External Context
	Reactions

- Environment determines the external opportunities or constraints a person has to react to. Relates to the *where* and *when* of genius.

- Behaviors are the specific actions or reactions made by a person within the environment. Relates to the *what* of genius.

- Capabilities guide and give direction to behavioral actions through a mental map, plan or strategy. Relates to the *how* of genius.

- Beliefs and values provide the reinforcement (motivation and permission) that supports or inhibits capabilities. Relates to the *why* of genius.

- Identity involves a person's role, mission and/or sense of self. Relates to the *who* of genius.

- Spiritual involves the larger system of which one is a part and the influence of that system on healing. Relates to the *who else and what else* of genius.

Strategies

NLP focuses on the structure of the *mental programming* at the base of a person's thinking process rather than on the products of that programming. Much of the NLP approach to the mind is based on viewing the brain as functioning similar to a computer in certain ways. In fact, much of the NLP terminology (and the name itself) incorporates the language of computer science.

A *'strategy'* is like a program in a computer. It tells you what to do with the information you are getting, and like a computer program, you can use the same strategy to process a lot of different kinds of information. A computer program might tell the computer, "take this piece of data and take that piece of data, to add them together and put the answer in a particular place in memory". The program is independent of the content being processed through it. It doesn't care what content is being put together and moved. Some programs are more efficient than others; some allow you to do more with the information than others; some are designed to take a lot of information and reduce it to very tightly chunked information. Other computer programs are designed to take some information and make projections with it. Some programs are designed to find patterns and features within information.

The same thing is going to be true of human strategies. As an analogy, they are the mental software used by the bio-computer of the brain. In one way, the most powerful personal computer in the world is the one that sits up between your ears. The problem with it is that it didn't come with a user's manual, and sometimes the software isn't very "user friendly." The goal of psychology, and in particular NLP, is to unveil more about the "programming language" of the human nervous system so we can act more elegantly, effectively and ecologically. One of the basic purposes of this work on *Strategies of Genius* is to study some of the 'software' created by people like Albert Einstein who have learned to operate that computer very effectively.

Micro, Macro and Meta Strategies

Strategies occur at different levels - there are micro-strategies, macro-strategies and meta-strategies.

- A micro-strategy focuses on how exactly a particular person is thinking within a specific moment in order to accomplish a particular task. If somebody is engaging in a process of remembering a particular piece of information, let's say a telephone number, what do they do with that information in order to store it and recover it from within their brain or bio-computer? On this micro-level you might want to know exactly what size that person is visualizing the telephone number in his or her mind. Is there a particular color in which that person pictures the number? Does the person verbally repeat the number internally? Does the person have a feeling somewhere in his or her body? This would be a micro-strategy.

- A macro-strategy would be more like modeling "success" or "leadership". An overall strategy for success or leadership is not going to be a micro-strategy but rather a higher level program that will incorporate many micro strategies. It might be something that takes place over a much longer period of time. Sometimes it is the more general steps of a process that are important for reaching a particular result, and how specifically you get from A to B to C on a micro-level is not important or may require significant variation. What is important is that you get from A to C regardless of the micro steps. The way you personally get there is up to you. So a macro-strategy would have to do with the more general operations and steps of a thinking process.

- A meta-strategy or a meta-model is basically a model for making models; a strategy for finding strategies, or a model for modeling. In a sense, a major part of what you are going to be learning in this book is a meta-model and a set of meta-strategies - strategies and models for finding the strategies of exceptional individuals and making practical models out of those strategies.

In this study of Einstein, we will be exploring all three levels of Einstein's thinking process; Micro, Macro and Meta. My plan is to:

1) begin with an overview of Einstein's basic meta strategy or 'epistemology',

2) examine some of the basic macro principles of his own process for creating scientific theories and models,

3) explore the general structure of his thinking process and his views on thinking and the role of language,

4) make a micro analysis of some of the specific representational elements of Einstein's thinking process,

5) explore the cognitive processes behind his famous theory of relativity,

6) discuss some of the wider implications of relativity and Einstein's strategy for relativistic thinking, and

7) conclude with some ways to apply his strategies and beliefs to our everyday lives and problems.

In this way I hope to "deal with the problem of the 'how' " and convert some of the 'miracle' of Einstein's accomplishments into "something that may be grasped" and used to enrich our lives.

Footnotes to Introduction

1. Albert Einstein, *"Autobiographical Notes,"* in **Albert Einstein, Philosopher-Scientist** by Paul Arthur Schilpp, Northwestern University Press, Evanston, Ill., 1949, p. 32.

2. Albert Einstein, *"Isaac Newton,"* in **Out of My Later Years,** The Citadel Press, Secaucus, New Jersey, 1956, pp 219-220.

Chapter 1

Einstein's Epistemology

An *"epistemology"* is an underlying system of knowledge from which all other knowledge is derived. A person's "epistemology" then, is the system of fundamental presuppositions and beliefs from which that person operates. It is the "Meta-Strategy" through which one generates all one's other strategies. This belief system both shapes and is derived from one's life experiences and underlying mental processes. In essence, an epistemology is a description of the most fundamental motives and purposes that influence and guide a person's actions. These beliefs, values and goals will strongly contribute to the development of a person's capabilities and personality. Exploring Einstein's epistemology thus provides a basic insight into the structure and development of his genius.

Einstein was once asked to explain why he had chosen to get into the field of physics. Rather than cite a desire for a Nobel prize, a specific interest in the velocities of atoms or photons or the distance of specific stars, etc., he answered:

> *"I want to know how God created this world. I am not interested in this or that phenomenon, in the spectrum of this or that element; I want to know his thoughts; the rest are details."* [1]

Einstein's statement implies that *"God's thoughts"* would be the most fundamental, practical and elegant "forms" or "patterns" in the universe around us. Like Aristotle, Einstein felt compelled to constantly search for more and more basic and far reaching relationships in our universe - its 'basic conditions' and 'first principles'. In fact, he devoted the last two decades of his life to what he called the *"unified field theory"* - an attempt to discover the common laws governing everything in the universe, from electrons to the planets. The "unified field theory" attempted to relate the universal properties of matter and energy in a single equation or formula (unfortunately he never successfully completed this final stage of his life's work).

Einstein believed in, and strove to make explicit, the fundamental connectedness and unity in the universe. He claimed that *"God reveals himself in the harmony of what exists,"* and made it his life's work to make some of that harmony explicit. Although he was a 'scientist', Einstein was, in the deepest sense, a spiritual person. Yet his conception of 'God' was broader and more encompassing than that of most organized religions. He maintained:

> *"For the [naive man] God is a being from whose care one hopes to benefit and whose punishment one fears; a sublimation of feeling similar to that of a child for its father, a being to whom one stands to some extent in a personal relation, however deeply it may be tinged with awe.*

> *"But the scientist is possessed by the sense of universal causation. The future, to him, is every whit as necessary and determined as the past...His religious feeling takes the form of a rapturous amazement at the harmony of natural law, which reveals an intelligence of such superiority that, compared with it, all the systematic thinking and acting of human beings is an*

utterly insignificant reflection. This feeling is the guiding principle of his life and work, in so far as he succeeds in keeping himself from the shackles of selfish desire. It is beyond question closely akin to that which has possessed the religious geniuses of all ages." [2]

Einstein's comments indicate that his perception of God was more spiritual than 'religious' in nature. Rather than support or impose any particular religious *or* scientific beliefs, Einstein's strategies were geared toward unveiling "the harmony of natural law." As we shall see, this involved the ability to integrate together what seemed to be fundamentally opposite frames of reference. While this process was most clearly illustrated in his *theory of relativity*, it extended into all areas of his life. For instance, as a scientist, there were certain age old issues and conflicts he strove to resolve.

"During the last century, and part of the one before, it was widely held that there was an unreconcilable conflict between knowledge and belief. The opinion prevailed among advanced minds that it was time that belief should be replaced increasingly by knowledge; belief that did not itself rest on knowledge was superstition, and as such had to be opposed...

"It is true that convictions can best be supported with experience and clear thinking...[however] those convictions which are necessary and determinant for our conduct and judgments, cannot be found solely along this solid scientific way.

"For the scientific method can teach us nothing else beyond how facts are related to and conditioned by, each other." [3]

Here Einstein brings up the seemingly fundamental opposition between personal "beliefs" or "faith" and "scientific knowledge." These two ways of thinking have traditionally been thought to be incompatible and even antagonistic. Scientists thought belief to be superstitious, idealistic, impractical, and *"much too vague that we should be able to draw from [them] with confidence specific rules to guide the individuals in their actions."*[4] Science, on the other hand was viewed by the layman as mechanistic, dry, disassociated, even mercenary.

Even though he was himself a scientist, however, Einstein acknowledged that the scientific method alone was not enough to act effectively and appropriately in the world. The main deficit of science, according to Einstein, was that:

> *"Science searches for relations which are thought to be independent of the searching individual. This includes the case where man himself is the subject...The concepts which it uses to build up its coherent systems are not expressing emotions. For the scientist, there is only 'being,' but no wishing, no valuing, no good, no evil; no goal...he keeps away from everything voluntaristic or emotional. Incidentally, this trait is the result of a slow development, peculiar to modern Western thought."*[5]

Before Einstein, scientists looked out at the world around them and measured and described it, leaving out any influence on that world that they might have had as observers. Even scientists studying psychological processes seemed to ignore the effect that their own presence had on the creatures they were studying. For instance, Ivan Pavlov never considered the effect of his own relationships with his dogs as having an influence upon the effects of his experiments. He meticulously controlled the light in the room, the sound in the room, the vibrations in the room, but it was as if he himself didn't exist as anything to his dogs other than a stimulus. It was as if to say, "My attitude, my relationship to the dog has no effect on his behavior."

The biggest problem with this approach is that, while it can provide us with effective means for accomplishing certain ends independent of the observer or "searching individual," it does not necessarily provide us with the information needed to determine appropriate or ecological ends for the whole *system* of observed and observer. Einstein maintained:

> *"[K]nowledge of what is does not open the door directly to what should be. One can have the clearest and most complete knowledge of what is, and yet not be able to deduct from that what should be the goal of our human aspirations...[O]ur existence and our activity acquire meaning only by the setting up of such a goal and of corresponding values."* [6]

Einstein seems to be echoing Aristotle's notion of final causes - that in living systems *purpose directs activity.* The ability to manipulate symbols, make observations and measurements or build tools does not make a genius, or a good human being. Beliefs, ethics and wisdom have to do with the setting of fundamental goals. In fact, Einstein once wrote that:

> *"Perfections of means and confusion of goals seem - in my opinion - to characterize our age."* [7]

According to the great American psychologist William James:

> *"The pursuance of future ends and the choice of means for their attainment are thus the mark and criterion of the presence of mentality in a phenomenon."* [8]

Similarly, in NLP we conceive of the sequence of cognition and sensory processes that define a particular mental strategy as organized into a basic feedback loop called a T.O.T.E. (Miller, et al, 1960). The letters **T.O.T.E.** stand for *Test-Operate-Test-Exit*. The T.O.T.E. concept maintains that all mental and behavioral programs revolve around having a *fixed goal* and a *variable means to achieve that goal*. Thus, the basic processes involved in thinking are (**T**)esting information from the senses in order to check progress towards the goal then (**O**)perating to change some part of the ongoing experience so that it can satisfy the (**T**)est and (**E**)xit on to the next part of the program.

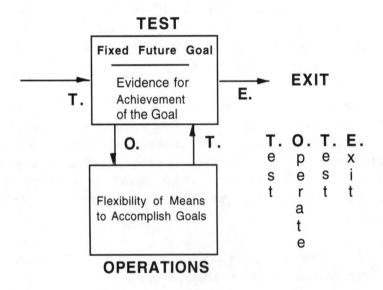

From its extensive study of effective people from all fields, NLP has identified three qualities that characterize all successful and creative individuals that parallel James' definition:

1) They have a fixed goal that guides their actions.

2) They have a close feedback loop with sensory experience to test their progress toward their goal.

3) They have flexibility of behavior so that they can vary their actions appropriately in order to achieve their goals with the maximal ease and efficiency.

Einstein implies that scientific methods can tend to rigidify its means or procedures and produces a variable goal, instead of the other way around. Scientific descriptions generally revolve around identifying chains of cause-and-effect that are traced backwards to past precipitating events (what Aristotle called 'antecedent' or 'mechanical' causes). The notion of "final causes" - that events are triggered by future goals - is not allowed as valid scientific thinking. Yet, ethics and intelligence are a function of goals and 'finality'. As William James said:

"In all ages the man whose determinations are swayed by reference to the most distant ends has been held to possess the highest intelligence."[9]

According to the T.O.T.E. model, our beliefs and values should be the 'Test' phase of our life programs, and our knowledge and technical methods should be the 'Operations' we use to achieve those higher level goals.

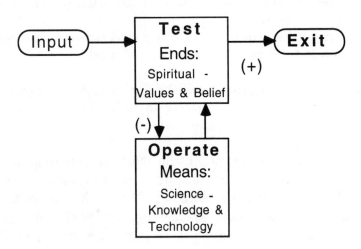

In fact, it is from this perspective that Einstein begins to unify and harmonize the relationship between knowledge and beliefs, and religion and science:

> *"Science is the century-old endeavor to bring together by means of systematic thought the perceptible phenomena of this world into as thorough going an association as possible...*

> *"[R]eligion is the age-old endeavor of mankind to become clearly and completely conscious of [fundamental - RD] values and goals and constantly to strengthen and extend their effect...*

> *"If one conceives of religion and science according to these definitions then a conflict between them appears impossible. For science can only ascertain what is, but not what should be...Religion, on the other hand, deals only with evaluations of human thought and action: it cannot justifiably speak of facts and relationships between facts."* [10]

Einstein is saying that the functions of religion (beliefs and values) and science (knowledge and technical capability) are on two completely different levels and therefore cannot conflict - unless we mistakenly collapse or confuse the two levels (which has certainly happened many times in the course of human history). If one is able to recognize the two different levels, however, the two processes can support rather than conflict with one another.

"Now, even though the realms of religion and science in themselves are clearly marked off from each other, nevertheless there exists between the two strong reciprocal relationships and dependencies. Though religion may be that which determines the goal, it has, nevertheless, learned from science in the broadest sense, what means will contribute to the attainment of the goals it has set up. But science can only be created by those who are thoroughly imbued with the aspiration towards truth and understanding. This source of feeling, however, springs from the sphere of religion" [11]

According to Einstein, it is the spiritual sense of mission and purpose (which does not relate to the mechanics of 'what is') that is the source and motivation for further scientific development. And that scientific developments and tools should be used in service of the deeper purpose or mission that inspired those developments.

Einstein elegantly sums up the interrelation between science and religion with the statement:

"Science without religion is blind, religion without science is lame." [12]

Just as Einstein interwove the relationship between matter and energy, waves and particles, and the moving and stationary observer, he synthesized together scientific and ethical processes.

> *"Scientific statements of facts and relations, indeed, cannot produce ethical directives. However, ethical directives can be made rational and coherent by logical thinking and empirical knowledge. If we can agree on some fundamental ethical propositions, then other ethical propositions can be derived from them, provided that the original premises are stated with sufficient precision. Such ethical premises play a similar role in ethics, to that played by axioms in mathematics."* [13]

Einstein is maintaining that while the *content* of science and ethics is different, the *form* is the same. Facts and empirical knowledge deal with the mechanics of our behavior and environment. Ethical premises and directives address our beliefs, values and identity. Yet while these issues are on different levels, the mental processes which determine our capability to use them are on the same level. The way in which one derives and applies ethical relationships can be similar to the way in which one derives and applies scientific relationships. Einstein provides the following example.

> *"In the case of lying this might perhaps be done in some way such as this: Lying destroys confidence in the statements of other people. Without such confidence, social cooperation is made impossible or at least difficult. Such cooperation, however, is essential to make human life possible and tolerable. This means that the rule 'Thou shalt not lie' has been traced back to the demands: 'Human life shall be preserved' and 'Pain and sorrow shall be lessened as much as possible'."* 14

Similar to Aristotle, Einstein's strategy involved connecting specific behaviors and phenomenon to deeper 'first principles'. And, like Aristotle, Einstein contended that the 'first principles' of both science and ethics were not actually possible to figure out from the content of our experience, but must be arrived at by imagination and intuition. Then they could be assessed according to their pragmatic value.

> "For pure logic all axioms are arbitrary, including the axioms of ethics. But they are by no means arbitrary from a psychological and genetic point of view. They are derived from our inborn tendencies to avoid pain and annihilation, and from the accumulated emotional reactions of individuals to the behavior of their neighbors." [15]

As with scientific knowledge, ethical beliefs must maintain a constant feedback loop with sensory experience. Beliefs may not be possible to derive from experience, but they must serve us in experience:

> "Ethical axioms are found and tested not very differently from the axioms of science. Truth is what stands the test of experience." [16]

Einstein emphasized the necessity of constant feedback with sensory experience. The coherent organization of behavior and sensory experience is the whole purpose for ethics and science to begin with and thus is the ultimate test of success.

Moral behavior, according to Einstein, was a function of the continual feedback loop between ethical beliefs, scientific reasoning and our sensory experience. Rather than a dogmatic system of rules and restrictions, it was a living organic process that was constantly rejuvenating itself.

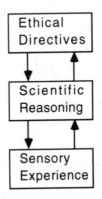

"Morality in the sense here briefly indicated is not a fixed and stark system. It is rather a standpoint from which all questions which arise in life could and should be judged. It is a task never finished, something always present to guide our judgment and to inspire our conduct." [17]

In systems theory there is a principle called *the law of requisite variety* (Ashby, 1956) which has deep implications for both science and ethics. According to the law of requisite variety we need to be constantly exploring variations in the operations and the processes that we use to get desired results within a particular context. Even processes that have been effective in the past might not continue to be effective if the environment or the system around it changes. It's easy to believe that because something was successful before, it will continue to be successful. But if there are changes in the system around it, those things which used to work will no longer continue to function.

The law of requisite variety states that *"in order to successfully adapt and survive, a member of a system needs a certain minimum amount of flexibility, and that flexibility has to be proportional to the potential variation or the uncertainty in the rest of the system."* In other words, if someone is committed to accomplishing a certain goal, that person needs to have a number of possible ways to accomplish it. The number of different ways needed to reach the goal depends upon the amount of change that is possible within the system in which one is attempting to achieve the goal.

A key issue in both science and ethics is how to balance processes such as change, diversity and uncertainty with values such as 'consistency' and 'congruency' in behavior. The answer has to do with where we put the flexibility. If one is consistent with respect to one's goal, one will have to have flexibility in how he or she reaches the goal. The issue has to do with at which levels are we flexible. In one sense, where you need to be flexible is determined by where you are determined to be inflexible. If somebody is determined to be competent at, say, leading or motivating people, then that is what they're holding constant. Where they need the flexibility is being able to adapt to different motivations of people, and different environments.

As an analogy, let's say a musician wants to be consistent in producing a certain kind of sound with a certain kind of quality. This person has to be able to adapt to the acoustical variation of different concert halls, different musical instruments, etc. To be truly competent, one needs to have flexibility in certain areas and inflexibility in others.

According to the law of requisite variety, wisdom, ethics and ecology do not derive from having the one 'right' or 'correct' map of the world, because human beings are not capable of making one. Rather, the goal is to create the richest map possible that respects the systemic nature and ecology of ourselves and the world in which we live.

In NLP, in fact, 'ecology' is considered to be an even deeper principle than 'ethics', in that what is 'ethical' for one person or from one perspective, may be harmful or unethical for another person, or for another part of the larger system in which that person is a participant. The challenge of 'ecology' is to have a rich and wide enough map and strategy to be able to track enough elements and dynamic variations within a system to be able to act 'ecologically'.

In many ways Einstein's approach to both science and ethics is more suited to the manner in which our neurology functions than either a mechanistic or dogmatic system. The architecture of the nervous system is set up similarly to that of a homing device. Once given a goal it begins a self correcting feedback loop that homes in on the goal. When you stand up, write your name, or speak, for instance, you do not consciously focus on all of the minute muscle adjustments, shifts in balance, focusing of our eyes, etc. We simply focus on where we want to be or what we want to do (the 'final cause') and our nervous systems automatically makes the adjustments necessary to accomplish it. Any static system, whether it originates in science or religion, ends up working against this fundamental principle of the human nervous system. And, in Einstein's view, they also work against the fundamental principles of the human spirit.

"[T]he ancients knew something which we seem to have forgotten. All means prove but a blunt instrument, if they have not behind them a living spirit. But if the longing for the achievement of the goal is powerfully alive within us, then we shall not lack the strength to find the means for reaching the goal and for translating it into deeds." [18]

"If we desire sincerely and passionately the safety, the welfare and the free development of the talents of all men, we shall not be in want of the means to approach such a state. Even if only a small part of mankind strives for such goals, their superiority will prove itself in the long run." [19]

Einstein's statement about the *"safety, the welfare and the free development of the talents of all men,"* brings up another important element of Einstein's epistemology. He was well known as a great humanitarian. He is also known for his humility and modesty regarding his own accomplishments. In spite of his fame and reputation as a genius, he was never reported to have acted the least bit egotistical or superior. Einstein was able to put himself in other people's perspectives and see himself in the humanity around him. As he stated:

> *"Every man has his own cosmology and who can say that his own theory is right"* [20]

One of the basic principles of Neuro-Linguistic Programming is that every person has his or her own unique model of the world, and that no one model of the world is any more valid than any other model of the world. These models are our own internal 'maps' of the external 'territory'. Because we don't operate directly on the world around us but rather through representations of that world that come through our senses, we can never directly know reality, only our maps of it. As Einstein claimed:

> *"The real nature of things, we shall never know, never."* [21]

The goal of making one's model of the world is not to find the one 'true' or 'real' map, but rather to build a model that allows for the most richness, choice and co-ordination with the other models of the world of the people around us.

> *"For looked at from the simple human point of view, moral conduct does not mean merely a stern demand to renounce some of the desired joys of life, but rather a sociable interest in a happier lot for all men.*

"This conception implies one requirement above all - that every individual should have the opportunity to develop the gifts which may be latent in him...For everything that is really great and inspiring is created by the individual who can labour in freedom. Restriction is justified only in so far as it may be needed for the security of existence.

"There is one other thing which follows from that conception - that we must not only tolerate differences between individuals and between groups, but we should indeed welcome them and look upon them as an enriching of our own existence." [22]

In this comment, Einstein is essentially applying the principle of 'Requisite Variety' to the notion of 'morality'. Rather than be a rigid set of mechanical rules that prescribed the 'right way to act', Einstein maintained that the final cause of 'morals', was "a happier lot for all men". According to the law of requisite variety, achieving this goal requires not only the tolerance of, but the encouragement of individual and cultural diversity in order to account for and adapt to variation and change within different people and environments.

In his theory of relativity, Einstein contended that no one view of the universe was any more 'real' than any others. Einstein generalized that belief to his personal life as well. He maintained:

"So long as they don't get violent, I want to let everyone say what they wish, for I have always said exactly what pleases me." [23]

Yet, while Einstein respected and accepted all points of view as having as much validity of his own, he was not apathetic nor anarchistic. He did not have a, *"Why bother, its all relative anyway,"* attitude. The fact that perceptions change relative to the position of the observer doesn't mean perception is false or arbitrary. According to the law of requisite variety, change on one level implies stability on another. For example, while NLP believes that everyone has a different model of the world, it also believes that there is an underlying content-free structure that defines the unchanging generating rules for **how** these models are built and organized. While our perceptions are actually a mixture of sense experiences, imaginary constructs and metaphors that are all subject to distortion, there are deeper forms and principles underlying this content that do not change. The purpose for having a diversity of maps, perspectives and capabilities is to support the achievement of deeper level values and goals.

Einstein reflected this principle in his social views, in which he strove to integrate the relationship between the individual and society.

"The individual, if left alone from birth, would remain primitive and beast-like in his thoughts and feelings to a degree that we can hardly conceive. The individual is what he is and has the significance that he has not so much in virtue of his individuality, but rather as a member of a great human society, which directs his material and spiritual existence from the cradle to the grave.

"A man's value to the community depends primarily on how far his feelings, thoughts, and actions are directed towards promoting the good of his fellows. We call him good or bad according to how he stands in this matter, It looks at first sight as if our estimate of a man depended entirely on his social qualities.

"And yet such an attitude would be wrong. It is clear that all the valuable things, material, spiritual and

moral, which we receive from society can. be traced back through countless generations to certain creative individuals. The use of fire, the cultivation of edible plants, the steam engine — each was discovered by one man.

"Only the individual can think, and thereby create new values for society — nay, even set up new moral standards to which the life of the community conforms. Without creative, independently thinking and judging personalities the upward development of society is as unthinkable as the development of the individual personality without the nourishing soil of the community." [24]

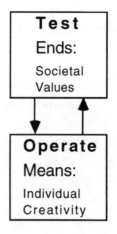

So, like belief and knowledge, or religion and science, society and the individual functioned at different levels to form a positive feedback loop. With society functioning as the "test" phase, and the individual performing the creative "operations" to help achieve the higher level goals.

To Einstein, individual imagination, curiosity and creativity were (in conjunction with feedback from sensory experience) the primary means of evolving and reaching goals. Creativity and imagination are probably the first and most important feature of genius. Imagination allows us to reach where our senses cannot go. When this process was used in the service of all of humankind one was achieving one's highest purpose.

> *"The highest principles for our aspirations and judgments are given to us in the Jewish-Christian religious tradition...If one were to take that goal out of its religious form and look merely at its purely human side, one might state it perhaps thus: free and responsible development of the individual, so that he may place his powers freely and gladly in the service of all mankind.*
>
> *"There is no room in this for the divinization of a nation, of a class, let alone of an individual. Are we not all children of one father, as it is said in religious language."* [25]

Thus, while Einstein valued and respected everyone's points of view, there were certain behavioral results of some models that he could not justify from any perceptual position. Violence and war was one means to an end that Einstein could neither justify nor integrate. His purpose was to identify the processes of order, harmony and creation, not destruction. As he adamantly maintained:

> *"Warfare cannot be humanized. It can only be abolished"* [26]
>
> *"Atomic energy has created a new world in which balance-of-power politics have become utterly meaningless. Mankind must give up war in the atomic era. What is at stake is the life or death of humanity."*

Yet, ironically, Einstein's own discoveries and creativity lead to the development of one of the most powerful and deadly weapons of destruction in existence - the atomic bomb.

Certainly, one might be tempted to ask , "How, then, is one supposed to operate in and deal with a world in which nothing can be known with certainty? A world that is supposed to reflect the harmony of 'God's thoughts' but is capable of producing illness, crime, torture and the destruction at Hiroshima? If reality is indeed 'relative' how do we stay secure, sane and in control?"

There is, in fact, an anecdote about Einstein that addresses some of these questions. It describes how Einstein was once approached by a reporter during an interview and asked something to the effect of, *"Dr. Einstein, you are recognized around the world as one of the most bone fide geniuses of our century, maybe of human history. Your scope of thinking has covered the workings of the universe from the tiny atom to the cosmos. You have seen your discoveries both evolve and enrich, and also mutilate and destroy the human life you so highly value. What, in your opinion is the most important question facing humanity today?"*

Characteristically, Einstein stared off into space for a moment, and then looked down at the ground in front of him. Finally he looked back at the reporter and replied, *"I think the most important question facing humanity is, 'Is the universe a friendly place?' This is the first and most basic question all people must answer for themselves.*

For if we decide that the universe is an unfriendly place, then we will use our technology, our scientific discoveries and our natural resources to achieve safety and power by creating bigger walls to keep out the unfriendliness and bigger weapons to destroy all that which is unfriendly - and I believe that we are getting to a place where technology is powerful enough that we may either completely isolate or destroy ourselves as well in this process.

"If we decide that the universe is neither friendly nor unfriendly and that God is essentially 'playing dice with the universe,' then we are simply victims to the random toss of the dice and our lives have no real purpose or meaning.

"But if we decide that the universe is a friendly place, then we will use our technology, our scientific discoveries and our natural resources to create tools and models for understanding that universe. Because power and safety will come through understanding its workings and its motives."

As Einstein was so fond of saying:

"God is subtle but he is not malicious" [27]

Einstein's comment about the decision as to whether or not the universe is a "friendly place" reflects a deep principle in NLP which states that, at some level, all behavior is adaptive or "positively intended." That is, all behavior is or was perceived as appropriate or necessary from the "actor's" point of view, given the context in which it was established and the model of the world of that person. People make the best choices available to them given the possibilities and capabilities that they perceive to be accessible within their model of the world. Any behavior, no matter how evil, crazy or bizarre it seems, is perceived by the person as the best choice available at that point in time. In their first book, ***The Structure of Magic Vol. I***, Richard Bandler and John Grinder (the co-creators of NLP) pointed out:

[P]eople who respond creatively and cope effectively...are people who have a rich representation or model of their situation, on in which they perceive a wide range of options in choosing their action. The other people experience themselves as having few options, none of which are attractive to them...What we have found is not that the world is too limited or that there are no choices,

but that these people block themselves from seeing those options and possibilities that are open to them since they are not available in their models of the world. [28]

Thus, people do not do bad things because they are inherently bad, but rather because they have a narrow or limited model of the world. It has been said, "Never ascribe to maliciousness what can be much more easily explained as stupidity." Einstein humorously maintained, *"Only two things are infinite, the universe and human stupidity, and I'm not sure about the former."* If a person has a positive intention to change something for the better but believes that the only means available to produce change is through violence, then the positive intention will translate into acts of violence.

According to NLP, the goal is to validate people's positive intentions and constantly strive to widen and enrich their models of the world. This will allow them to be able to perceive more choices for achieving their positive intentions. That is one of my basic reason's for modeling Einstein and writing this book. Possibly more than any other person in the last century, Einstein has helped to widen our view of our world and our universe.

Perhaps the best way to sum up Einstein's epistemology is with the following statement, which encapsulates so much of his world view:

"A human being is a part of the whole called by us 'universe'...a part limited in time and space. He experiences his thoughts and feelings as separated from the rest — a kind of optical delusion of his consciousness. This delusion is a kind of prison for us, restricting us to our personal desires and to affection for a few persons nearest us. Our task must be to free ourselves from this prison by widening our circle of compassion to embrace all living creatures and the whole of nature in its beauty."

Like NLP, Einstein is maintaining that our mission is to 'free ourselves' from the 'prisons' created by the limitations of our own models of the world by widening our perceptual maps of that world. Einstein implies that the universe is like a kind of 'hologram'. A hologram is a 3-dimensional image in which the whole picture is contained in every part of the image. If you cut a hologram in half, at first it will appear as if you have lost part of the image. But if you change your perspective and tilt the holographic film you will see that the rest of the image is still there. To see it you simply need to change your angle of view. If you cut the half of the hologram in half again, the same thing will happen. If you don't change your point of view, more of the image will appear to have been lost. But if you keep tilting the image to different angles, you will find that the rest of the image is still there. If you continue to cut the hologram into smaller and smaller pieces the same thing happens. The whole image may still be seen in each piece of the hologram, provided you tilt it at the appropriate angles in order to see it.

What Einstein is saying is that human beings (and indeed all living creatures and all aspects of nature) are like a tiny piece of a holographic universe. If you keep one limited perspective you will have the delusion that it is just one tiny separate piece. But if you are able to look deeply enough into it from enough different perspectives you will see that the whole picture is contained within each piece.

Similar to NLP, Einstein is maintaining that the individual is a part of a larger system and that 'life' and 'mind' are ultimately *systemic* processes; in other words, that the processes that take place within a human being and between human beings and their environment are systemic. Our bodies, our societies, and our universe form an ecology of complex systems and sub-systems, all of which interact with and mutually influence each other. It is not possible to completely isolate any part of the system from the rest of the system.

On the one hand, such systems are based on certain 'self-organizing' principles and naturally seek optimal states of balance or homeostasis. It is in the best interests of the members of the system to preserve the ecology of the whole. On the other hand, the actors in the system do not always perceive or identify with the system as a whole, and take actions that actually work against their own best interests and the interests of the larger system. A violent father who abuses his wife or child in order to get 'respect' has a positive intention, but is only identified with and perceiving the situation from his small part of the total system.

Similarly, an ethnic group that commits genocide against another may have the positive intent to insure their own survival and preserve their sense of identity, but are operating from an impoverished world view that focuses only upon their small part of a larger system. And, in both cases, the actors may be unwittingly working against their own positive intentions. The violent father may succeed in getting only hatred and resistance instead of respect. The intolerant society may, in fact, be condemning themselves and confusing or contaminating an otherwise healthy sense of identity by their brutality to their fellow human beings. Whatever degree of 'success' they achieve will be only on the behavioral level and for the short term.

Einstein claims our task must be to widen "our circle of compassion" to free ourselves from the self imposed prison of our own ignorance. Of course, this is easier said then done. To accomplish this task we need new tools and technologies, not simply good intentions and nice wishes. To widen our "circle of compassion" we must widen our maps of the world; and our models of the world are built upon many unconscious assumptions and presuppositions that we perceive as being 'reality'. Albert Einstein had a uniquely effective strategy for identifying and challenging basic assumptions about our perceptions of the world. By modeling that strategy and applying it to other situations and contexts, I hope to be able to contribute to the task and mission so eloquently expressed and embodied by Einstein himself.

Footnotes to Chapter 1

1. *ALBERT EINSTEIN: A Portrait,* Pomegranate Calendars & Books, Corte Madera, CA, 1984, p. 3.

2. Albert Einstein, *"The Religiousness of Science",* **The World As I See It,** The Citadel Press, Secaucus, New Jersey, 1934, p. 29.

3. Albert Einstein, *"Science and Religion,"* **Out of My Later Years,** The Citadel Press, Secaucus, New Jersey, 1956, p. 21.

4. Albert Einstein, *"Morals and Emotions,"* **Out of My Later Years,** The Citadel Press, Secaucus, New Jersey, 1956, p. 17.

5. Albert Einstein, *"The Laws of Science and the Laws of Ethics,"* **Out of My Later Years,** The Citadel Press, Secaucus, New Jersey, 1956, p. 114.

6 . Albert Einstein, *"Science and Religion,"* p. 22.

7. Albert Einstein, *"The Common Language of Science,"* **Out of My Later Years,** The Citadel Press, Secaucus, New Jersey, 1956, p. 111.

8. William James, *Principles of Psychology,* **Britannica Great Books,** Encyclopedia Britannica Inc., Chicago Ill., 1979, p. 5.

9. William James, *Principles of Psychology,* p. 15.

10. Albert Einstein, *"Science and Religion,"* pp. 24-25.

11 . Albert Einstein, *"Science and Religion,"* p. 26.

12. Albert Einstein, *"Science and Religion,"* p. 26.

13. Albert Einstein, *"The Laws of Science and the Laws of Ethics,"* pp. 114-115.

14. Albert Einstein, *"The Laws of Science and the Laws of Ethics,"* p. 115.

15. Albert Einstein, *"The Laws of Science and the Laws of Ethics,"* p. 115.

16. Albert Einstein, *"The Laws of Science and the Laws of Ethics,"* p. 115.

17. Albert Einstein, *"Morals and Emotions,"* p. 19.

18 . Albert Einstein, *"Science and Religion,"* p. 24.

19. Albert Einstein, *"The Common Language of Science,"* p. 113.

20. ***ALBERT EINSTEIN: A Man for All Seasons,*** Pomegranate Calendars & Books, Corte Madera, CA, 1987, p. 14.

21. ***ALBERT EINSTEIN: A Man for All Seasons,*** p. 16.

22. Albert Einstein, *"Morals and Emotions,"* p. 19.

23. ***ALBERT EINSTEIN: A Man for All Seasons,*** p. 6.

24. Albert Einstein, *"Society and Personality"*, ***The World As I See It,*** The Citadel Press, Secaucus, New Jersey, 1934, pp. 8-9.

25. Albert Einstein, *"Science and Religion,"* p. 23.

26. ***ALBERT EINSTEIN: A Man for All Seasons,*** p. 10.

27. Donald Clarke, ***Great Inventors & Discoveries,*** Marshall Cavendish Books Limited, London, 1978, p. 64.

28. Bandler, R. & Grinder, J.; ***The Structure of Magic Vol. 1,*** Science and Behavior Books, Palo Alto, CA, 1975, pp. 13-14.

Chapter 2

Einstein's Macro-Strategy for Modeling

Einstein was more than a scientist, he was a "modeler." Modeling differs from other types of theory building in that its concern is not with "objective truth," "reality" or "statistical validation" but rather with "practicality," "simplicity" and "choice." As Einstein pointed out:

> *"Science is the attempt to make the chaotic diversity of our sense-experience correspond to a logically uniform system of thought. In this system single experiences must be correlated with the theoretic structure in such a way that the resulting coordination is unique and convincing."* [1]

> *"The aim of science is, on the one hand, a comprehension, as complete as possible, of the connection between the sense experiences in their totality, and, on the other hand, the accomplishment of this aim by the use of a minimum of primary concepts and relations."* [2]

Einstein is proposing that progress and intelligence in the model making process comes from the ability to connect the model with a larger and larger scope of sensory experiences, but also from increased elegance and simplicity within the model itself. As he claimed:

"A theory is the more impressive the greater the simplicity of its premises is, the more different kinds of things it relates, and the more extended its area of applicability." [3]

One of the dangers in modeling, however, is being too abstract or "reductionistic" - that is, getting so caught up in the model or theory itself that one loses contact and feedback with sensory experience. This can lead to generalization, deletion and distortion. As Einstein so elegantly advised:

"Everything should be made as simple as possible, but not simpler." [4]

If it is made too simple, it becomes *simplistic*.

On the other hand, if we limit ourselves to only what can be directly sensed and measured, as we are building new models, there is a tendency to become caught up in content and details. Our models become more descriptive in nature than generative.

Challenging Basic Assumptions

In order to conduct our lives and solve problems, we are all constantly making models of our experiences. The question is, when to simplify those models versus when are they too simple. Einstein constantly sought to find the limiting assumptions that either made our thinking too simplistic or not simple enough. As he was fond of saying:

"Our thinking creates problems that the same type of thinking will not solve."

Einstein maintained that when we thought about something we often made tacit assumptions about things that we have come to take for granted. While these assumptions generally help to short cut our thinking and keep it from becoming too cumbersome, they can limit us if we forget that they are there. For instance, consider the following problem:

A boy and his father were in an automobile accident. The boy's father sustained only minor injuries and sat anxiously in the waiting room while the boy was taken into the emergency room at the hospital. The emergency room doctor came rushing in to assist the boy but stopped abruptly and exclaimed, "I can't operate on this boy. He's my son!" Who was the emergency room doctor?

Many people in Western culture still have the unconscious assumption that doctors are primarily men. This causes quite a few individuals to hesitate for a moment before arriving at the most obvious answer that the emergency room doctor is the boy's mother. Some even become baffled, or venture guesses such as the boy has a step father, etc.

Einstein believed that it was these kinds of assumptions about reality that created problems for us more so than reality itself.

Theoretical physicist David Bohm points out that one of the problems with contemporary physics (and scientific model making in general) is that it has become merely a way of describing what our instruments can measure.

> *"...we mostly look at the equations and just work out what our instruments will do and how our instruments will give results according to these equations."*

> *"...only what could be measured by an instrument could be considered real, because the only point about the reality of physics is the results of instruments..."* [5]

Bohm points out that the problem with this is that the process of measurement often deletes or *"subtracts out"* important and fundamental background or contextual information because:

> *"...the instruments do not directly respond to this background. Because they are floating in it. It's like a fish not being aware of the ocean."* [6]

Einstein certainly echoed this in his theory of relativity in which he demonstrated that the frame of reference from which one was operating while making a measurement actually changed the measurement, and pointed out that in general *"the operation of measurement introduces unknown elements"*. In fact, the **Heisenberg Uncertainty Principle** in physics states that the act of measuring something actually changes what is possible to know about the thing itself. So that when we measure one aspect of something we automatically screen out the ability to measure another aspect of it. For example, we can measure how **fast** an atomic particle is going, but that makes it impossible to know exactly **where** it is; or, we can measure exactly where the particle is, but that then makes it impossible to know exactly how fast it is going.

The response of modern physics to this has been to assume that since we can't really know anything for certain about reality, we must resign ourselves to figure out what will happen "on the average" through statistical descriptions.

For a person who strove to know "God's thoughts", such as Einstein, this was not an acceptable solution. Claiming that *"God does not play dice with the universe,"* Einstein maintained that statistical models were only necessary when one did not understand the true underlying generative rules, patterns and principles of all the systems involved, claiming:

> *"The statistical character of the present theory would then have to be a necessary consequence of the incompleteness of the description of the systems in quantum mechanics."* [7]

For Einstein, the incompleteness of the statistical way of thinking comes from not realizing that *"the theory, in reality, does not operate with the single system, but with a totality of systems."*[8] Since some of the systems in the "totality of systems" have been left out of the description or model being used, their actions influence the ones included in the model in a way that appears random or only statistical. As an analogy, consider the following problem: Which of the following numbers is most different from the others?

1) One
2) Thirteen
3) Thirty-One

While there is no "right" answer to this problem, if we only consider the system of written numbers, we will be forced to make up answers in attempt to arbitrarily argue why 'one', 'thirteen', or 'thirty-one' is special or unique in some way. If, on the other hand, we realize that the 1), 2) and 3) are also numbers, the number 2 becomes an obvious solution, because it is the only even number and refers to neither a one nor a three as do all of the other numbers.

Einstein felt that the seemingly random nature of our observations of reality were not because reality itself was random, but rather because we were leaving out some other part of the whole system, as in the two systems of numbers in the problem above. To Einstein, statistics were only necessary when some critical influence had been left out of the total system being modeled.

"It is the aim of science to establish general rules which determine the reciprocal connection of objects and events in time and space. For these rules, or laws of nature, absolutely general validity is required - not proven. It is mainly a program, and faith in the possibility of its accomplishment in principle is only founded on partial successes.

"To be sure, when the number of factors coming into play in a phenomenological complex is too large scientific method in most cases fails us. One need only think of the weather, in which case prediction even for a few days ahead is impossible. Nevertheless no one doubts that we are confronted with a causal connection whose causal components are in the main known to us. Occurrences in this domain are beyond the reach of exact prediction because of the variety of factors in operation, not because of any lack of order in nature.

"We have penetrated far less deeply into the regularities obtaining within the realm of living things, but deeply enough nevertheless to sense at least the rule of fixed necessity. One need only think of the systematic order in heredity, and in the effect of poisons, as for instance alcohol, on the behavior of organic beings. What still is lacking here is a grasp of connections of profound generality, but not a knowledge of the order itself." [9]

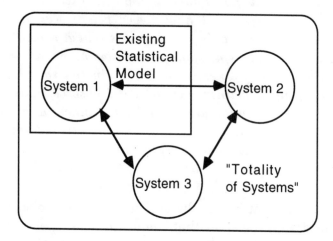

Einstein's point is that just because we have not yet formulated the laws governing a particular phenomenon, does not mean that the order isn't there. Furthermore, the fact that we cannot predict the weather accurately does not mean that the laws of physics are invalid, nor is it simply random or statistical. Rather, our grasp of all the systems involved is simply incomplete.

Einstein felt that, in the same way, the underlying laws of the universe were not random or statistical and that we must not give up the search for simple but broad rules defining the basic relationships between things. To explain his point of view, Einstein made the following analogy:

"I am standing in front of a gas range. Standing alongside of each other on the range are two pans so much alike that one may be mistaken for the other. Both are half full of water. I notice that steam is being emitted continuously from the one pan, but not from the other. I am surprised at this even if I have never seen either a gas range or a pan before. But if I now

*notice a luminous something of bluish color under the
first pan but not under the other, I cease to be
astonished, even if I have never before seen a gas
flame. For I can only say that this bluish something
will cause the emission of the steam, or at least
possibly it may do so. If, however, I notice the bluish
something in neither case, and if I observe that one
continuously emits steam whilst the other does not,
then I shall remain astonished and dissatisfied until I
have discovered some circumstance to which I can
attribute the different behavior of the two pans."*[10]

Einstein's point is that the basic rules we use to operate in
the world, and the rules that the world itself operates from,
are not always observable through the content of our experience. But just because we cannot directly sense or measure
them does not mean that such rules or causal connections are
not there. Rather than resign himself to make a statistical
description of the probabilities of steam rising from either of
the pans, Einstein strove to find the underlying order be-
neath phenomena and experiences which seemed inexpli-
cable.

Einstein pointed out that statistical models tend to use
linear laws to describe the phenomena they are trying to map
out, and thus *"contain no assertions concerning the **interaction** of elementary bodies. The true laws cannot be linear nor
can they be derived from such."*[11] In the language of Aristotle,
Einstein is contending that there are 'constraining' causes as
well as 'antecedent' causes which must be considered in the
systems we are attempting to model.

Furthermore, one of the biggest problems with models that
are primarily based upon measurement and statistics is that
they are *descriptive* as opposed to *generative*. As David
Bohm points out, *"the statistics of quantum mechanics is
nothing but an algorithm for cranking out how our instruments are going to operate,"*[12] and thus doesn't lead us to

more fundamental discoveries. His and Einstein's fear is that *the more impactful and important is often sacrificed for the more measurable.* (This is no doubt true for many fields other than physics. It is, in fact, the same issue NLP has contended with in regard to many of the existing psychological models and methods.) A model should be a process tool whose function is to be useful in gaining a broader survey of all of our experiences. It should lead us somewhere, in addition to providing us with descriptions.

In contrast to a descriptive model, a *generative* model has a very small number of basic rules that interact together to produce an infinite variety of combinations and results. Human language, for example, has a small finite number of rules of grammar that allow us to combine together a relatively small number of words to produce an infinite number of sentences and ideas.

Cybernetics is a field whose purpose is to study the interactions between systems and elements within a system. In his article *The Second Cybernetics*, Maguroh Maruyama elegantly defines the issue and dilemma Einstein constantly sought to address in his objection to statistical quantum mechanics. In a discussion of the growth and development of biological systems, Maruyama maintains:

> *"The amount of information to describe the resulting pattern is much more than the amount of information to describe the generating rules and positions of the initial tissues. The pattern is generated by the rules and by the interactions between the tissues. In this sense, the information to describe the adult individual was not contained in the initial tissues at the beginning but was generated by their interactions."* [13]

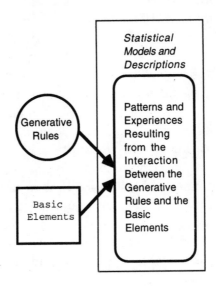

In terms of Maruyama's description, Einstein felt that statistical models were more focussed on describing the "resulting pattern" than on finding the "generating rules" that interacted to create the resulting pattern. Thus, Einstein, like Bohm, believed that they offered *"no useful point of departure for further development."*[14] He felt that to accept a descriptive, statistical model was to give up hope of finding the fundamental, unifying laws that determined **how** the universe functioned.

Einstein believed that, in order to find the "generating rules" of physical phenomena, a process other than those employing just statistics or measurements must be used. As Maruyama points out:

"...it is in most cases impossible to discover the simple generating rules after the pattern has been completed, except by trying all possible sets of rules. When the rules are unknown, the amount of information needed

to discover the rules is much greater than the amount of information needed to describe the rules. This means there is much more waste, in terms of the amount of information, in tracing the process backwards than in tracing it forwards. A geneticist would waste much time and energy by trying to infer the characteristics of the embryo from the characteristics of the adult organism." [15]

The problem with trying to trace the process "forward," however, is that the closer we get to the actual patterns that create the structure of our universe, the farther we get from anything that we can directly sense or experience. We cannot actually see, hear or feel atomic particles interacting with one another, nor can we directly perceive *"gravitational"* or *"electromagnetic"* forces. We can only perceive and measure their results. We postulate the imaginary construct *"gravity"* to explain the effects. Einstein believed that concepts such as *"gravity," "electromagnetic force," "atoms," "cause-and-effect," "energy,"* even *"time"* and *"space"* were in many ways just arbitrary constructs that came from our imagination (not the outside world) in order to categorize and put order to our sense experiences. He wrote that:

"Hume saw clearly that certain concepts, as for example that of causality, cannot be deduced from the material of experience by logical methods...All concepts, even those which are closest to experience, are from the point of view of logic freely chosen conventions." [16]

What Einstein is saying here is that our senses do not actually perceive things like "causes", they can only perceive that first one event happened and then another event happened right after the first one. For example, we may perceive a sequence of events such as, first, *'a man chops on a tree with an axe'* and then *'the tree falls down',* or *'a woman says something to a child'* and then *'the child starts crying',* or *'there is an eclipse of the sun and then an earthquake the next day'.* According to Einstein, we can say that "the man caused the tree to fall down," "the woman caused the child to cry" or "the eclipse caused the earthquake," but that only the **sequence** of the events is what is perceived - **"cause"** is a freely chosen internal construct that we apply to the relationship we perceived. For instance, one could just as easily say, "gravity caused the tree to fall," "the child's unfulfilled expectations caused him to cry" or "forces from inside the earth caused the earthquake" depending on which frame of reference we choose to take.

Einstein's point is that the basic rules we use to operate in the world, and the rules that the world itself operates from, are not observable through the content of our experience. As he summarizes:

> *"A theory can be tested by experience, but there is no way from experience to the setting up of a theory."* [17]

This same dilemma applies with equal force to psychology, neurology, and probably every area of human endeavor. *The closer we get to the actual primary relationships and rules that determine and run our experience, the further we are from anything that is directly perceivable.* We cannot physically sense the fundamental principles and rules that generate our behavior and experiences, only their effects. When the brain, for instance, tries to perceive itself, there will be certain unavoidable blind spots.

Again, since it is not possible to derive the fundamental principles from experience alone, statistical descriptions and measurements won't lead us to these basic laws. We must use an alternative process. In contrast to the statistical model of quantum mechanics, Einstein suggests that rather than trying to build our models or maps of the world strictly from measurements and statistics, since we can never know the territory directly anyway, the most appropriate strategy for evolving new models is by freely creating new maps of the world through imagination and "free thinking" and then test their validity through observation.

> *"Physics constitutes a logical system of thought which is in a state of evolution, whose basis cannot be distilled, as it were, from experience by an inductive method [i.e., one that traces backwards from experience - RD], but can only be arrived at by free invention. The justification (truth content) of the system rests in the verification of the derived propositions by sense experiences, whereby the relations of the latter to the former can only be comprehended intuitively. Evolution is proceeding in the direction of increasing simplicity of the logical basis. In order to approach this goal, we must resign to the fact that the logical basis departs more and more from the facts of experience, and that the path of our thought from the fundamental basis to those derived propositions, which correlate with sense experiences, becomes continually harder and longer."* [18]

This is why Einstein claimed that imagination and "free play with concepts" were so important. These processes could open doorways that measurements and statistics could not even perceive. In a way, imagination actually brings us closer to the actual mechanics and structure of how we perceive. Imagination comes more from our brain structures than from outside experiences. Since all of our world models are built by our brain structures, those which are most effective are those which most closely match and fit in with the way our brain is structured and operates naturally. Since imagination derives more fully from our internal neurological structures, it can often create the best 'fit'.

Einstein went so far as to say that:

> *"...all our thinking is of this nature of free play with concepts; the justification for this play lies in the measure of survey over the experience of the senses which we are able to achieve with its aid. The concept of "truth" can not yet be applied to such a structure."*[19]

> *"In guiding us in the creation of such an order of sense experiences, success alone is the determining factor."* [20]

Notice that Einstein is saying the theory should be adjusted to fit our sensory experience (not just our measurements and statistics). Too often, theoreticians do just the opposite and adjust their experiences, measurements and statistics to fit their theory.

Einstein summarizes his entire modeling process when he writes:

> *"I see on the one side the totality of sense-experiences, and, on the other, the totality of the concepts and propositions which are laid down in books.*

> *"The relations between the concepts and propositions among themselves and each other are of a logical nature, the business of logical thinking is strictly limited to the achievement of the connections between concepts and propositions among each other according to firmly laid down rules, which are the concern of logic.*

> *"The concepts and propositions get 'meaning,' viz., 'content,' only through their connection with sense-experiences. The connection of the latter with the former is purely intuitive, not itself of a logical nature. The degree of certainty with which this connection, viz., intuitive combination, can be undertaken, and*

nothing else, differentiates empty phantasy from scientific 'truth.'

"*The system of concepts is a creation of man together with the rules of syntax, which constitute the structure of the conceptual systems.*

"*Although the conceptual systems are logically entirely arbitrary, they are bound by the aim to permit the most nearly possible certain (intuitive) and complete co-ordination with the totality of sense-experiences; secondly they aim at greatest sparsity of their logically independent elements (basic concepts and axioms), i.e., undefined concepts and underived (postulated) propositions.*"[21]

Footnotes to Chapter 2

1. Albert Einstein, *"The Fundaments of Theoretical Physics,"* **Out of My Later Years**, The Citadel Press, Secaucus, New Jersey, 1956, p. 98.

2. Albert Einstein, *"Physics and Reality,"* in **Ideas and Opinions,** Crown Books, New York, NY, 1954. p. 293.

3. Albert Einstein, *"Autobiographical Notes,"* **Albert Einstein, Philosopher-Scientist** by Paul Arthur Schilpp, Northwestern University Press, Evanston, Ill., 1949, p. 33.

4. **EINSTEIN: A Portrait,** Pomegranate Calendars & Books, Corte Madera, CA, 1984.

5. Renee Weber, **The Enfolding-Unfolding Universe: A Conversation with David Bohm,** *Re•Vision,* Summer/Fall 1978, p. 30.

6. Renee Weber, **The Enfolding-Unfolding Universe**, p. 30.

7. Albert Einstein, *"Autobiographical Notes,"* p. 87.

8. Albert Einstein, *"Physics and Reality,"* p. 318.

9. Albert Einstein, *"Science and Religion,"* **Out of My Later Years**, The Citadel Press, Secaucus, New Jersey, 1956, p. 28.

10. Albert Einstein, **Relativity,** Crown Publishers, Inc., New York, NY, 1961, p. 72.

11. Albert Einstein, *"Autobiographical Notes,"* p. 89.

12. Renee Weber, **The Enfolding-Unfolding Universe**, p. 32.

13. M. Maruyama, *"THE SECOND CYBERNETICS: Deviation-Amplifying Mutual Causal Processes,"* in **American Scientist,** Vol. 51, 1963, p. 174.

14. Albert Einstein, *"Autobiographical Notes,"* p. 87.

15. M. Maruyama, *"THE SECOND CYBERNETICS,"* p. 174.

16. Albert Einstein, *"Autobiographical Notes,"* p. 13.

17. Albert Einstein, *"Autobiographical Notes,"* p. 89.

18. Albert Einstein, *"Physics and Reality,"* p. 322.

19. Albert Einstein, *"Autobiographical Notes,"* p. 7.

20. Albert Einstein,*"Physics and Reality,"* p. 292.

21. Albert Einstein, *"Autobiographical Notes,"* p. 13.

Chapter 3

The Basic Structure of Einstein's Thinking Strategy

While Einstein's chosen area was physics, we all find ourselves in the kind of problem solving dilemma described in relationship to his scientific work. We are confronted with a problem in the form of some kind of symptom, but the causes of the symptom are not directly perceivable, either because of the complexity of the system or because we have not considered all of the parts of the system that may contribute to the "problem space." As an example of the same kind of process being addressed by Einstein but in an area that is unrelated to physics, consider the following organizational problem that might face an upper level manager in a company:

You are the person in charge of factory "B". The chief of your maintenance Department manages 6 eight man teams, working under 6 foremen. You are worried because these teams don't work efficiently. As a matter of fact, the workers in the teams tend to do just what strictly concerns their specific tasks. As a result, work and programs of this Department are slowed down. Only in cases of emergency is this routine overcome. You also know, on the other hand, that the capabilities and competence of the workers are higher and allow for more effective utilization.

Whether you work as a manger in an organization or not, take a moment and consider how you would approach solving this problem. Before you continue on, make some notes about your ideas. We will return to this problem later on and it will be interesting to discover if your thinking about it changes.

An interesting question that you may have already asked yourself is "How would a genius like Einstein have approached this problem?" Until recently, most of us would probably have dismissed this question as being unanswerable, or, if answerable, too difficult and confusing for the average person to follow. Through the psychological modeling techniques of NLP, however, we can gain new insights into the thought patterns and processes that contributed to Einstein's special genius in a way that can make them more available to us. By uncovering some of the underlying micro elements of his thinking strategy, we can better understand and more easily transfer Einstein's creative ability.

Perhaps the best place to begin our examination of these elements is with Einstein's own ideas about the processes of 'thinking', 'cognition' and the 'mind'. While Einstein may have been a physicist and not a psychologist, he certainly qualifies as an expert user of psychological processes. And in fact, Einstein was no stranger to the field of psychology. He was studied and questioned many times regarding his theoretical discoveries, and had contact with some of the greatest psychologists of our century. In addition to his extensive interviews with Gestalt psychology founder Max Wertheimer, who questioned Einstein *"in great detail about the concrete events in his thought,"[1]* Einstein also participated in a substantial written correspondence with Sigmund Freud regarding fundamental elements of individual and social psychology and their implications for world peace.

In addition to giving us insight into Einstein's personal view of the mind, Einstein's 'thoughts about thinking' can also provide us with some important clues to the psychological processes behind his genius.

When most people think of Einstein, they think of compli-
cated mathematical formulas - incoherent scribbles understood only by a few esoteric physicists; something completely
out of the grasp of the average person. Yet, according to
Einstein himself, his actual creative thinking process didn't
seem to involve mathematics at all.

> *"No really productive man thinks in such a paper
> fashion. The way the two triple sets of axioms are
> contrasted in the Einstein-Infeld book [on relativity -
> RD] is not at all the way things happened in the
> process of actual thinking. This was merely a later
> formulation of the subject matter, just a question of
> how things could afterwards best be written. The
> axioms express essentials in a condensed form. Once
> one has found such things one enjoys formulating
> them in that way; but in this process [the development
> of the theory of relativity - RD] they did not grow out of
> any manipulation of axioms."[2]*

Rather than glorify his own mental accomplishments or
shroud them behind the complexities of mathematical formulas, Einstein claimed that, *"The whole of science is nothing
more than a refinement of everyday thinking."* [3]
Like NLP, Einstein related the basic process of everyday
thinking to the stimulation and reactivation of sensory
experience.

> *"Our psychological experience contains, in colorful
> succession, sense experiences, memory pictures of them,
> images, and feelings. In contrast to psychology, physics
> treats directly only of sense experiences and of the
> 'understanding' of their connection. But even the
> concept of the 'real external world' of everyday thinking
> rests exclusively on sense impressions."* [4]

Einstein differentiated between 1) "sense experiences" coming as input from our environment 2) "memory pictures" or impressions left by the sense experiences we have received, 3) "images" (presumably of internal origin as opposed to 'sense experiences' which come from the 'external world') and 4) "feelings" (which would be our subjective reactions to the sense experiences, memories and images). To Einstein, these four categories form the total group of experiences from which we select and make combinations in order to build our mental models of the world.

From the NLP standpoint it is interesting to note that his definition is highly visual (i.e., *"colorful* succession", "memory *pictures", "images")*. He mentions feelings, but makes no reference at all to the auditory or verbal representational systems.

And in fact, Einstein claimed that for his most important discoveries language (verbal or mathematical) played little if any role at all. In an interview with Max Wertheimer on the development of the theory of relativity, Einstein claimed:

> *"These thoughts did not come in any verbal formulation. I very rarely think in words at all. A thought comes, and I may try to express it in words afterward.' When I [Wertheimer] remarked that many report that their thinking is always in words, he only laughed."[5]*

Instead of words or mathematical formulas, Einstein claimed to think primarily in terms of visual images and feelings. In a letter to cognitive psychologist Jacques Hadamard, Einstein explained:

"The words or the language, as they are written or spoken, do not seem to play any role in my mechanism of thought. The psychical entities which seem to serve as elements in thought are certain signs and more or less clear images which can be 'voluntarily' reproduced and combined.

"There is, of course, a certain connection between those elements and relevant logical concepts. It is also clear that the desire to arrive finally at logically connected concepts is the emotional basis of this rather vague play with the above mentioned elements. But taken from a psychological viewpoint, this combinatory play seems to be the essential feature in productive thought - before there is any connection with logical construction in words or other kinds of signs which can be communicated to others.

"The above mentioned elements are, in my case, of visual and some of muscular type. Conventional words or other signs have to be sought for laboriously only in a secondary stage, when the mentioned associative play is sufficiently established and can be reproduced at will...[My typical thinking style is] visual and motoric. In a stage when words intervene at all, they are, in my case, purely auditive, but they interfere only in a secondary stage as already mentioned." [6]

What Einstein is saying is that the verbal or mathematical representation of his thoughts came only **after** the important creative thinking was done. His actual creative thinking took place through internal visual images (notated V^i in NLP - for **V**isual **i**nternal) and "motor" or "muscular" kinesthetic sensations (notated **K** in NLP for **K**inesthetic).

It was only after the imagery was sufficiently well developed, that it was translated into verbal or mathematical expression - notated A_d in NLP (for **A**uditory **d**igital). It is interesting to note that he even uses the term "interfere" to describe the way words fit into his strategy.

In Einstein's strategy, then, the organization and exploration of information takes place through the "combinatory play" of visual images and body sensations. The auditory digital (i.e., verbal) system is used primarily to evaluate the results of the "play" according to "logical" rules for connecting the elements together, and then to output or express the constructions made through the **Visual—>Kinesthetic** loop.

Internally generated feelings or emotions (notated **K^i** for internal **k**inesthetic sensations) seem to serve as the motivational access and guiding system in the strategy as is indicated by Einstein's statement that *"the **desire** to arrive finally at logically connected concepts is the **emotional** basis of this rather vague play."* These feelings seem to give information about the relative 'connectedness' (and presumably also the lack of connection) between the visual and kinesthetic 'play' and the more logical verbal and mathematical models:

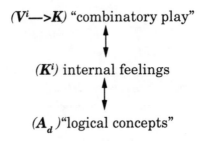

(V^i—>K) "combinatory play"

(K^i) internal feelings

(A$_d$) "logical concepts"

Einstein explained the role of these internal feelings more fully when he stated:

"During all those years there was a feeling of direction, of going straight toward something concrete. It is, of course, very hard to express that feeling in words; but it was decidedly the case, and clearly to be distinguished

*from later considerations about the rational form of
the solution. Of course, behind such a direction there
is always something logical; but I have it in a kind of
survey, in a way visually."* [7]

What Einstein is saying here is that these 'guiding feelings' were functioning in coordination with some kind of
higher level 'big picture' - i.e., *"visual survey"*. This *"visual
survey"* —>*"feeling of direction"* process not only stood in
between the *"combinatory play"* and *"logical concepts"* processes but stood **above** and somehow influenced the
"combinatory play" process at a higher level - as a puppeteer
would control a marionette. The lower level play with the
visual and "muscular" or "motoric" kinesthetic elements were
operated by the higher and broader level visual survey and
more whole-body emotional sense of direction. As Wertheimer
summarized it:

*"Two directions are involved: getting a whole consistent
picture, and seeing what the structure of the whole
requires for the parts."* [8]

The following diagram summarizes what we have discussed about Einstein's strategy up to this point:

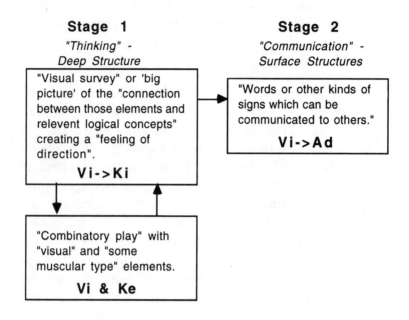

Diagram Outlining Einstein's Basic Thinking Strategy

Einstein gives a fairly explicit description of how his 'combinatory play' with images leads to the larger picture when he writes:

> *"What, precisely, is 'thinking?' When, at the reception of sense-impressions, memory-pictures emerge, this is not yet 'thinking.' And when such pictures form a series, each member of which calls forth another, this too is not yet 'thinking.' When, however, a certain picture turns up in many such series, then - precisely through such return - it becomes an ordering element for such series, in that it connects series which themselves are unconnected. Such an element becomes an instrument, a concept."* [9]

Just as Aristotle maintained, Einstein is saying that neither sensory input, the internal replication of sensory input in the form of "memory-pictures," nor even the connecting of sensory experiences through the process of association, are enough to account for the critical structuring of the thinking process. To Einstein the definitive element of 'thinking' is the "concept" - an "ordering element" that comes from noticing something which repeats in a number of experiences; the process Aristotle called "induction." In NLP we call this type of ordering element that connects a series of experiences a *"pattern."*

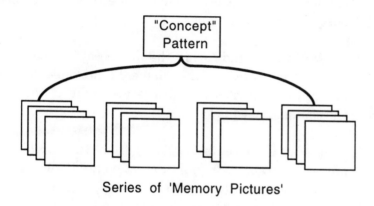

Series of 'Memory Pictures'

A "Concept" is an "Ordering Element" That Connects a Series of Experiences

We now have a general idea of how Einstein used the basic psychological processes he identified as fundamental for everyday thinking - i.e., "sense experiences," "memory pictures," "images," "feelings" and "language".

1) Sense experiences form the input into the strategy (V^e, A^e, K^e).

2) These sensory experiences leave memory pictures (V^r) which enter into a 'combinatory play' with constructed imagery (V^c) through a process of association stimulated by muscular and motoric activity (K^e).

3) The numerous sequences of images that result from this play are related to a larger "visual survey" (V^i) through "concepts" which have been discovered inductively by noticing pictures which repeat and form an "ordering element" or a pattern which connects series of previously disconnected images.

4) A feeling (K^i) indicating the degree of 'completion' or 'connection' between the elements provides feedback and reinforcement which also serves to direct and shape the combinatory play.

5) The visual concepts resulting from the *combinatory play—> concept—>feeling* interaction are then related to logical (mathematical or verbal) concepts, evaluated and communicated through logically connected language models (A_d).

Footnotes to Chapter 3

1. Max Wertheimer, *Productive Thinking*, Greenwood Press, Westpoint, Connecticut, Enlarged Edition, 1959, p. 228.

2. Max Wertheimer, *Productive Thinking*, p. 228.

3. Albert Einstein, *"Physics and Reality,"* in *Ideas and Opinions,* Crown Books, New York, NY, 1954. p. 290

4. Albert Einstein,*"Physics and Reality,"* p. 290.

5. Max Wertheimer, *Productive Thinking*, p. 228.

6. Albert Einstein, *"Letter to Jacques Hadamard,"* *The Creative Process*, edited by Brewster Ghiselin, Mentor Books, New American Library, New York, New York, 1952, p. 43.

7. Max Wertheimer, *Productive Thinking*, p. 228.

8. Max Wertheimer, *Productive Thinking*, p. 212.

9. Albert Einstein,*"Physics and Reality,"* p. 291.

Chapter 4

Einstein's View of Language

Even though Einstein clearly separated his process of creative thinking from language, he acknowledged the importance of language as an influence in the process of thought and communication. He defined his basic view of the relationship between language and thought when he wrote:

"I think that the transition from free association or 'dreaming' to thinking is characterized by the more or less dominating role which the 'concept' plays in it. It is by no means necessary that a concept must be connected with a sensorially cognizable and reproducible sign (i.e., word); but when this is the case thinking becomes by means of that fact communicable."[1]

Here Einstein distinguishes between words and concepts, implying that they are fundamentally different - i.e., that words are not in themselves concepts but can become connected to them. Concepts do not need words in order to exist, but words are needed in order to communicate about concepts and experiences with others.

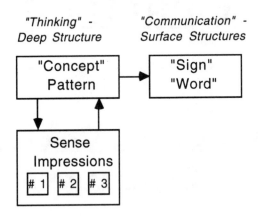

Words Are 'Surface Structures' Used To Communicate About Experiential 'Deep Structures'

Actually, Einstein's conception of language is remarkably similar to that proposed by NLP. NLP begins with a conception of language as a *"4-tuple."* That is, words or *'surface structures'* (A_d) are triggers for a group of stored sensory representations or *'deep structure'* from the four basic sensory channels: **V**isual, **A**uditory tonal, **K**inesthetic, and **O**lfactory. The basic relationship of language to experience is represented as $A_d < A_t, V, K, O >$; where the verbal surface structures (A_d) both trigger and are derived from the sensory deep structure represented by $< A_t, V, K, O >$.

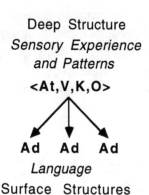

Deep Structure
*Sensory Experience
and Patterns*
<At,V,K,O>

Ad   Ad   Ad
Language
Surface   Structures

Verbal 'Surface Structures' Both Trigger and Are Derived From Sensory Experiences and Patterns

Einstein is in agreement with this notion when he writes:

"The first step towards language was to link acoustically or otherwise commutable signs to sense-impressions. Most likely all sociable animals have arrived at this primitive kind of communication - at least to a certain degree."[2]

This fundamental relationship between language and sense impressions is the essence of *"neuro-linguistics."* Of course, this basic linking is only the first step. As Einstein goes on to point out:

"A higher development is reached when further signs are introduced and understood which establish relations between those other signs designating sense-impression. At this stage it is already possible to report somewhat complex series of impressions; we can say that language has come to existence."[3]

What Einstein is referring to here is what might be called "meta language" - language about language. This would also be language not only about particular groups of sensory impressions but about the relationships, patterns or ordering elements which connect different sensory experiences together.

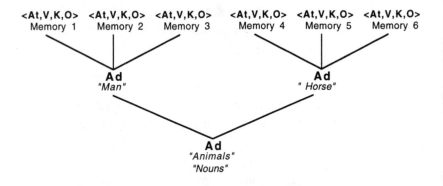

Words Stand For Relationships Between Experiences and Other Words

Once again, however, this trend towards abstraction emphasizes the need for feedback with external sensory input:

> *"If language is to lead at all to understanding, there must be rules concerning the relations between the signs on the one hand and on the other hand there must be a stable correspondence between the signs and impressions."*[4]

In addition to a *"stable correspondence"* between language and sensory experience, Einstein is also calling for *"rules concerning the relations between the signs"* - that is, some kind of separate internal coherency between the system of more abstract concepts. It is these rules which determine whether or not a sentence is 'well-formed' - i.e., the difference between *"The man rode the horse,"* and *"Rode the man horse."* These types of rules are the subject of the *"programming"* element of Neuro-Linguistic Programming.

Deep Structure
*Sensory Experience
and Patterns*

\<At,V,K,O\>

Rules of Transformation

Ad   Ad   Ad
Language
Surface Structures

Different Languages Have Different 'Rules of Transformation' Between Deep Structure and Surface Structures

Einstein continues:

"In their childhood individuals connected by the same language grasp these rules and relations mainly by intuition. When man becomes conscious of the rules concerning the relations between signs the so-called grammar of language is established."[5]

These rules of grammar are necessary to make a model, but Einstein makes it clear that the rules themselves have nothing to do with sensory reality. Different languages have different rules of grammar even though they are describing the same sensory reality. In fact Einstein equates the clarity of the rules with the degree of separation from sensory reality:

> *"In an early stage the words may correspond directly to impressions. At a later stage this direct connection is lost insofar as some words convey relations to perceptions only if used in connection with other words (for instance such words as: "is", "or," "thing"). Then word-groups rather than single words refer to perceptions. When language becomes thus partially independent from the background of impressions a greater inner coherence is gained.*
>
> *"Only at this further development where frequent use is made of so-called abstract concepts, language becomes an instrument of reasoning in the true sense of the word."[6]*

What Einstein is claiming is that it is only when language becomes sufficiently disassociated from the sensory experience that it was initially designed to represent, can it become a tool for creative thinking as opposed to a mere descriptive device. If we are to go beyond the limitations of our current sensory environment we must first have a way to break out of it, then we can rearrange it in new ways that we have never experienced directly before. For instance, the sentence, *"The man rode the horse,"* fits the grammatical rules of English and will most likely trigger "memory pictures" in most English speakers. Sentences like, *"The horse rode the man,"* or *"The man rode the light beam,"* however, fit grammatical rules but will more than likely require one to make internally constructed images in order to 'make sense' out of them.

Yet Einstein is quick to reiterate once again that the movement towards internal coherence and creativity must be balanced with feedback to sensory experience:

> *"But it is also this development which turns language into a dangerous source of error and deception. Everything depends on the degree to which words and word-combinations correspond to the world of impression."* [7]

So language and abstraction are a double edged sword - one edge allows us to create new models independent of the sensory content of our life experiences and to give a greater coherence and order to our experiences, but the other edge severs the all important connection between our conceptual maps and the sensory experience they are intended to organize (i.e., between such basic functions as logic and reality, map and territory, mind and body).

In their book ***The Structure of Magic Vol. I,*** Richard Bandler and John Grinder (the co-founders of NLP) echo Einstein's attitude and his concern about the use of language when they write:

> *The most pervasive paradox of the human condition which we see is that the processes which allow us to survive, grow, change, and experience joy are the same processes which allow us to maintain an impoverished model of the world - our ability to manipulate symbols, that is, to create models. So the processes which allow us to accomplish the most extraordinary and unique human activities are the same processes which block our further growth if we commit the error of mistaking the model of the world for reality. We can identify three general mechanisms by which we do this: Generalization, Deletion, and Distortion.*

Generalization is the process by which elements or pieces of a person's model become detached from their original experience and come to represent the entire category of which the experience is an example. Our ability to generalize is essential to coping with the world...The same process of generalization may lead a human being to establish a rule such as "Don't express any feelings."

Deletion is a process by which we selectively pay attention to certain dimensions of our experience and exclude others. Take, for example, the ability that people have to filter out or exclude all other sound in a room full of people talking in order to listen to one particular person's voice...Deletion reduces the world to proportions which we feel capable of handling. The reduction may be useful in some contexts and yet be the source of pain for us in others.

Distortion is the process which allows us to make shifts in our experience of sensory data. Fantasy, for example, allows us to prepare for experiences which we may have before they occur...It is the process which has made possible all the artistic creations which we as humans have produced...Similarly, all the great novels, all the revolutionary discoveries of the sciences involve the ability to distort and misrepresent present reality. [8]

Although our ability to use language and 'manipulate symbols' is clearly one of our distinguishing characteristics as a species, the potential problems created by the processes of generalization, deletion and distortion are great enough that Einstein is lead to question the need for language as an instrument of thinking at all:

"What is it that brings about such an intimate connection between language and thinking? Is there

*no thinking without the use of language, namely in
concepts and combinations for which words need not
necessarily come to mind? Has not everyone of us
struggled for words although the connection between
'things' was already clear?"* [9]

Einstein went so far as to write, *"our thinking goes on for
the most part **without** use of signs (words) and beyond that to
considerable degree unconsciously."*[10] In examining these statements from the NLP point of view, we can see that Einstein
is distinguishing between auditory digital and visual representational systems (i.e., struggling for *"words"* although the
connection is already *"clear"*). He is implying that verbal
representations are not essential for thinking, and perhaps
may even be secondary to the actual thinking process.
Secondly, he is pointing out that thinking also functions
independently of consciousness - that one does not need to be
consciously verbalizing to be thinking.

In defense of language, however, Einstein wrote:

*"We might be inclined to attribute to the act of thinking
complete independence from language if the individuals
formed or were able to form his concepts without the
verbal guidance of his environment. Yet most likely
the mental shape of an individual, growing up under
such conditions, would be very poor. Thus we may
conclude that the mental development of the individual
and his way of forming concepts depends to a high
degree upon language. This makes us realize to what
extent the same language means the same mentality.
In this sense thinking and language are linked
together."*[11]

The value of language then, according to Einstein, seems
to be in how it shapes our habitual way of forming concepts

rather than as a system of labeling concepts. As Grinder and Bandler point out:

> *"The nervous system which is responsible for producing the representational system of language is the same nervous system by which humans produce every other model of the world - visual, kinesthetic, etc...The same principles of structure are operating in each of these systems."[12]*

Thought of in this way, we can view the structure of our language systems as parallel to the structure of our other perceptual systems. Thus the structure and principles of language would in some way mirror the structure and principles of perception. The strategies for "forming concepts", though, would come more from the "principles of structure" (i.e., syntax or grammar) of the language than from the specific content of the vocabulary or words.

To Einstein, mathematical language also had vocabulary and grammar, but was a somewhat more universal form of expression than our verbal languages. What made mathematical language different from natural language was that it had become completely disassociated from the world of sense experiences:

> *"Mathematics deals exclusively with the relations of concepts to each other without consideration of their relation to experience."[13]*

This gives mathematics a greater simplicity and internal coherence than the world of sensory experience, and even of our verbal languages, because it is less influenced by the richness and diversity of the sensory world. In order to be practical, however, mathematical language had to be somehow connected to the world of experience. As Einstein explained it:

"Physics too deals with mathematical concepts; however, these concepts attain physical content only by the clear determination of their relation to the objects of experience."[14]

So, once again, the effectiveness of mathematical language, like all language, relies on the feedback loop it has with sensory experience. For Einstein, effective science seems to be a balance between the benefits of language, which primarily lie in its structure, and the benefits of sensory experience, which gives life to that structure.

"What science strives for is an utmost acuteness and clarity of concepts as regards their mutual relation and their correspondence to sensory data. As an illustration let us take the language of Euclidean geometry and Algebra. They manipulate with a small number of independently introduced concepts, respectively symbols, such as the integral number, the straight line, the point, as well as with signs which designate the fundamental operations, that is the connections between those fundamental concepts. This is the basis for the construction, respectively definition of all other statements and concepts.

"The connection between concepts and statements on the one hand and the sensory data on the other hand is established through acts of counting and measuring whose performance is sufficiently well determined."[15]

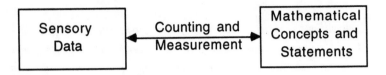

So, in the scientific method, mathematics is connected with the world of experience through the processes of counting and measurement - which, Einstein claims are "sufficiently well determined". Yet, even our most common methods of measurement are subject to generalization, deletion and distortion. In fact, some of Einstein's own most important contributions to science came from his challenging of the basic presuppositions behind our standard measurement of such things as space and time.

Footnotes to Chapter 4

1. Albert Einstein, *"Autobiographical Notes,"* **Albert Einstein, Philosopher-Scientist** by Paul Arthur Schilpp, Northwestern University Press, Evanston, Ill., 1949, p. 7.

2. Albert Einstein, *"The Common Language of Science,"* **Out of My Later Years**, The Citadel Press, Secaucus, New Jersey, 1956, p. 111.

3. Albert Einstein, *"The Common Language of Science,"* p. 111.

4. Albert Einstein, *"The Common Language of Science,"* p. 111.

5. Albert Einstein, *"The Common Language of Science,"* p. 111.

6. Albert Einstein, *"The Common Language of Science,"* pp. 111-112.

7. Albert Einstein, *"The Common Language of Science,"* p. 112.

8. Richard Bandler & John Grinder; **The Structure of Magic Vol. I,** Science and Behavior Books, Palo Alto, California, 1975, pp. 12-14.

9. Albert Einstein, *"The Common Language of Science,"* p. 112.

10. Albert Einstein, *"Autobiographical Notes",* p. 9.

11. Albert Einstein, *"The Common Language of Science,"* p. 112.

12. Richard Bandler & John Grinder; **The Structure of Magic Vol. I,** pp. 37-38.

13. Albert Einstein, *"The Theory of Relativity,"* **Out of My Later Years**, The Citadel Press, Secaucus, New Jersey, 1956, p. 41.

14. Albert Einstein, *"The Theory of Relativity,"* p. 41.

15. Albert Einstein, *"The Common Language of Science,"* pp. 112-113.

Chapter 5

Micro-Analysis of Einstein's Creative Thinking Process

We now have a general idea of how Einstein thought about and used the basic psychological processes he identified as fundamental for everyday thinking - i.e., "sense experiences," "memory pictures," "images," "feelings" and "language". Our next step is to take a closer look at how Einstein specifically employed some of these processes in his thinking strategy. Since Einstein claimed that the *"combinatory play seems to be the essential feature in productive thought"*, let us examine exactly how Einstein combined "memory pictures" and constructed "images" as he was thinking.

Rather than being abstract two-dimensional diagrams filled with symbols, Einstein's 'productive' images were typically more three-dimensional, metaphorical visualizations that he called "thought experiments." One clue to his specific way of using visualization has already been provided in the chapter on modeling through Einstein's analogy of the pans of water on the gas stove. In it Einstein is explaining a general principle with a simple visual metaphor.

A pattern Einstein used over and over again in his thinking strategy was forming a symbolic visual metaphor of some real world phenomenon and then questioning the assumptions presupposed by the symbolic construction.

For example, consider the almost dreamlike quality of the following "thought experiment" Einstein created in order to identify and challenge our assumptions about a basic phenomenon we typically take for granted, "gravity." He starts by asking, *"If we pick up a stone and then let it go, why does it fall to the ground?" The usual answer to this question is: "Because it is attracted by the earth."* Through an improbable fantasy, Einstein leads us to question that presupposition:

We imagine a large portion of empty space...far removed from the stars and other appreciable masses...As a reference body let us imagine a spacious chest resembling a room (such as an elevator) with an observer inside who is equipped with apparatus. Gravitation naturally does not exist for this observer. He must fasten himself with strings to the floor, otherwise the slightest impact against the floor will cause him to rise slowly towards the ceiling of the room.

To the middle of the lid of the chest is fixed externally a hook with a rope attached, and now a "being" (what kind of a being is immaterial to us) begins pulling at this with a constant force. The chest together with the observer then begin to move "upwards" with a uniformly accelerated motion. In course of time their velocity will reach unheard-of values — provided that we are viewing all this from another reference-body which is not being pulled with a rope.

But how does the man in the chest regard this process? The acceleration of the chest will be transmitted to him by the reaction of the floor of the chest. He must therefore take up this pressure by means of his legs if he does not wish to be laid out full length on the floor. He is then standing in the chest in exactly the same way as anyone stands in a room of a house on our earth. If he releases a body which he previously had in his hand, the acceleration of the chest will no longer be transmitted to this body, and for this reason the body will approach the floor of the chest with an accelerated relative motion. The observer will further convince himself that the acceleration of the body towards the floor of the chest is always of the same magnitude, whatever kind of body he may happen to use for the experiment.

Relying on his knowledge of the gravitational field, the man in the chest will thus come to the conclusion that he and the chest are in a gravitational field which is constant with regard to time. Of course he will be puzzled for a moment as to why the chest does not fall in this gravitational field. Just then, however, he discovers the hook in the middle of the lid of the chest and the rope which is attached to it, and he consequently comes to the conclusion that the chest is suspended at rest in the gravitational field.

Ought we to smile at the man and say that he errs in his conclusion? I do not believe we ought to if we wish to remain consistent; we must rather admit that his mode of grasping the situation violates neither reason nor known mechanical laws. [1]

From this intriguing 'imaginary construct' Einstein concluded that the 'gravitational mass' of an object (that determined by the attraction between matter) and the 'inertial mass' of an object (that determined by the movement of objects with respect to each other) were the same. In doing so he unified two previously separate conceptions about reality under a single definition. This change in conception has transformed the way physicists think about "concrete reality", yet Einstein arrived at it by taking an imaginary ride in an elevator pulled through space by some fantastic "being" (a much more interesting process than contemplating lines, arrows and equations).

Notice that, while the experience Einstein has created is a pure fantasy, he has filled in every last detail - from the strings on the traveller's feet to the hook in the lid of the chest. It is as if we can climb into the image along with Einstein and feel the "muscular" and "motoric" sensations of the traveller.

Another fascinating imaginary construct Einstein devised was one he used to challenge our assumptions about the structure of our universe. Most people tend to assume that the universe is an infinite three dimensional "Cartesian" space that extends out forever in straight lines. As opposed to linear boxes, Einstein came to visualize the universe as a kind of organic form that he referred to as a "mollusk". He devised a series of intriguing "thought experiments" challenging the assumption that the universe was infinite and flat.

[I]magine an existence in two dimensional space. Flat beings with flat implements, and in particular flat rigid measuring-rods, are free to move in a plane. For them nothing exists outside of this plane: that which they observe to happen to themselves and to their flat "things" is the all-inclusive reality of their plane. In particular, the constructions of plane Euclidean geometry can be carried out by means of rods...In contrast to ours, the universe of these beings is two-dimensional; but, like ours, it extends to infinity. In their universe there is room for an infinite number of identical squares made up of rods, i.e. its volume (surface) is infinite.

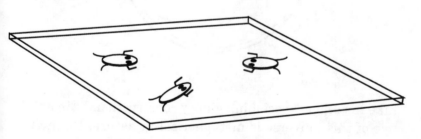

Let us now consider a second two-dimensional existence, but this time on a spherical surface instead of on a plane. The flat beings with their measuring-rods fit exactly on this surface and they are unable to leave it. Their whole universe of observation extends exclusively

over the surface of the sphere. Are these beings able to regard the geometry of their universe as being plane geometry and their rods withal as the realization of "distance"? They cannot do this. For if they attempt to realize a straight line, they will obtain a curve, which we "three-dimensional beings" designate as a great circle, i.e. a self-contained line of definite length, which can be measured up by means of a measuring rod. Similarly, this universe has a finite area that can be compared with the area of a square constructed with rods. The great charm resulting from this consideration lies in the recognition of the fact that the universe of these beings is finite yet has no limits. [2]

Like his other "special imaginary constructions" Einstein's image of this universe is metaphorical in nature. He invites us to become "two dimensional beings" sliding around a spherical universe. Rather than use logic or dry analytical speculations, we explore fundamental and supposedly abstract principles through our "impressions" and experience. We are drawn in by the fascination of the symbolism as much as the picture. We are interacting with other "beings" in other worlds, not with disassociated numbers and facts.

In another illustration his concept of a 'spherical universe' Einstein has us visualize, as an analogy, a blind beetle crawling around on a large globe (such as a basketball) suspended in space. The globe is so large in comparison to the beetle that the beetle perceives the surface as flat and linear. Also, because it is blind, the beetle cannot see any tracks that it has left. Thus, the beetle travels ever onward, unaware that it is going around and around in circles.

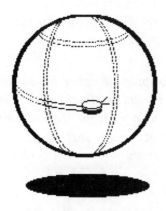

Again, this is certainly a more intriguing and robust type of visualization than the dry spots and squiggles of mathematical axioms. To Einstein, this imaging was the most important part of his thinking strategy. It provided a bridge between purely abstract logical symbols and words, and the *"chaotic diversity of our sense-experience."*

Once we had become familiar with such basic images, Einstein extended them to slightly more challenging dimensions.

To this two-dimensional sphere-universe there is a three-dimensional analogy, namely...three-dimensional spherical space. [3]

Einstein's process of starting with something that is relatively concrete and simple and then incrementally expanding
upon it (i.e., moving from flat two-dimensional space to a
sphere and finally to three-dimensional spherical space) is
called *"pacing and leading"* in NLP. 'Pacing' involves meeting
another person at their current capabilities and model of the
world. 'Leading' involves expanding and enriching through
small steps; each slightly more challenging than the previous
step, but with no step so large or difficult that the other
person becomes lost or confused.

Notice the way in which Einstein takes the next step in
expanding his image of space:

> *Is it possible to imagine spherical space?...Suppose we
> draw lines or stretch strings in all directions from a
> point...At first, the straight lines which radiate from
> the starting point diverge farther and farther from one
> another, but later they approach each other, and finally
> they run together again at a "counterpoint" to the
> starting point.   Under such conditions they have
> traversed the whole spherical space. It is easily seen
> that the three-dimensional spherical space is quite
> analogous to the two-dimensional spherical surface. It
> is finite (i.e. of finite volume), and has no bounds.* [4]

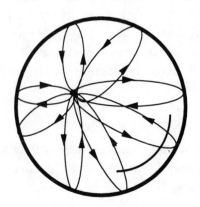

A next step would be to extend the image of radiating strings to a more complex shape of space, like Einstein's "mollusk."

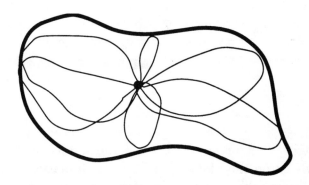

Another example of Einstein's process of 'pacing' and 'leading' is provided by a lecture he gave entitled *"Geometry and Experience."*   In his introduction to the lecture, he provocatively asks:

> *"Can we visualize a three-dimensional universe which is finite, yet unbounded?*
>
> *"The usual answer to this question is 'No', but that is not the right answer. The purpose of the following remarks is to show that the answer should be 'Yes'. I want to show that without any extraordinary difficulty we can illustrate the theory of a finite universe by means of a mental picture to which, with some practice, we shall soon grow accustomed."*[5]

Einstein goes on to lead the audience through a rather interesting and quite specific exercise in visualization. While the content is unimportant for our study, the basic strategy involves the setting up of a visual image of a glass globe on the flat surface of a plane - a simple three dimensional construction.

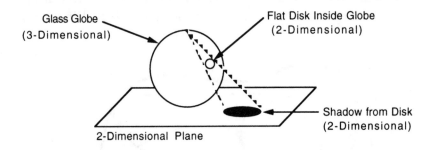

Einstein then proceeds to have the audience imagine a shadow cast on the plane by a flat, two-dimensional disk on the inside of the globe. He points out that the disk is restricted to a finite amount of movement because it is inside the globe. But the shadow it casts is unbounded in that it can extend out on the plane for an infinite distance according to the placement of the source of light.

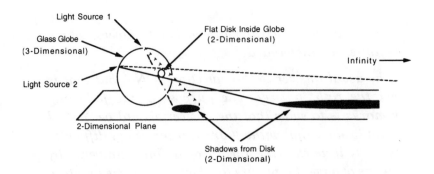

Einstein then has the audience imagine that a three-dimensional sphere was in the place of the two-dimensional disk and extend, through analogy, the relationship to a four dimensional globe. In other words, he has his students imagine a three-dimensional shadow cast by an sphere on a four-dimensional globe — an interesting and mind-bending experience.

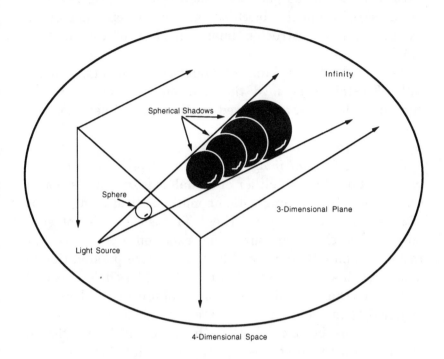

Einstein concludes the exercise by saying:

"In this way, by using as a crutch the practice in thinking and visualization which Euclidean geometry gives us, we have acquired a mental picture of spherical geometry. We may without difficulty impart more depth and vigour to these ideas by carrying out special imaginary constructions. Nor would it be difficult to represent the case of what is called elliptical geometry in an analogous manner. My only aim today has been to show that the human faculty of visualization is by no means bound to capitulate to non-Euclidean geometry." [6]

Here, Einstein has 'paced' and then 'lead' by using "memory pictures" of common objects to aid in the creation of an extraordinarily constructed "image" in a kind of "combinatory play".

As a result of these kinds of thought experiments, incidentally, Einstein concluded that our own universe may be curved in this way, as opposed to our typical linear conception of it, and that we, like the blind beetle, are unable to notice the tracks that we have left.

Einstein's *"special imaginary constructions"* are a type of visualization that is neither of actual sensory objects nor of completely abstract linguistic or mathematical symbols but of something in between. These 'fantasies' were not supposed to merely mimic our actual experience of reality, but rather to simplify and give life and creative possibilities to abstract thinking in a way that introduced less deletions and distortions than verbal or mathematical processes. This type of imaging can allow us to create mental maps that could help take us beyond what we have so far been able to experience with our senses. As Einstein pointed out:

> *"[A]tomic theory could be viewed more as a visualizing symbol than as knowledge concerning the factual construction of matter."* [7]

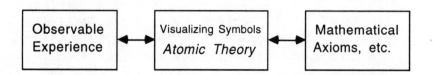

The mental image of the atom serves as a bridge between our rich but fluctuating sense experiences and precise but abstract mathematical axioms. 'Visualizing symbols' are easier to manipulate mentally because they simplify the complexity of our actual sensory experience and can be easily translated into mathematical descriptions. But on the other hand, they also resemble aspects of the sensory experience they are symbolizing, so they can be more easily and intuitively connected to sense experiences than a mathematical equation.

Perhaps the most important part of Einstein's imaginary constructions or 'visualizing symbols' is that they are not simply confusing abstract diagrams. They are metaphorical pictures that we can put ourselves into. We are in front of the stove, stumbling in the 'elevator' being pulled through space by some imaginary being, we are the flat beings in the two dimensional spherical world and the beetle eternally crawling around on the surface of the ball.

The purpose of those 'special imaginary constructions' was to add 'depth and vigor' to our concept of reality and ultimately to explore and expose what Aristotle called "formal causes." The "formal cause" of a phenomenon is that which gives the definition of its essential character. Formal causes relate our fundamental definitions and perceptions of something.

It was this kind of imaging and questioning that lead Einstein to his famous theory of relativity. Einstein responded that from the age of sixteen he began to wonder *what exactly would the world look like if he rode along on a light beam at the speed of light.* This was the seed that grew into the theory of relativity. Let's take a closer look at how the concept of relativity "came to birth" in Einstein's brain.

Footnotes to Chapter 5

1. Albert Einstein, *Relativity*, Crown Publishers, Inc., New York, NY, 1961. pp. 66-68

2. Albert Einstein, *Relativity*, pp. 108-109.

3. Albert Einstein, *Relativity*, p. 111.

4. Albert Einstein, *Relativity*, pp. 111-112.

5. Albert Einstein, "Geometry and Experience," **EINSTEIN: A Centenary Volume**, edited by A. P. French, Harvard University Press, Cambridge, Massachusetts, 1979, p. 294.

5. Albert Einstein, "Geometry and Experience," p. 297.

7. Albert Einstein, "Autobiographical Notes," **Albert Einstein, Philosopher-Scientist** by Paul Arthur Schilpp, Northwestern University Press, Evanston, Ill., 1949, p. 19.

Chapter 6

The Theory of Relati

As I mentioned earlier, before Einstein, scientists l
out at the world around them and measured and describe
leaving out any influence on that world that they might ha
had as observers. Einstein said that it was impossible t
delete the effect of the observer in the system even if the
system is purely physical, like particles and planets. He
maintained that the process of observing the system changes
the system.

For instance, physicists discovered that if you look at light
while you are measuring it, the light acts like it's made of
particles - matter. When you don't look at it when you are
measuring it, light acts like waves - energy. You change what
it is depending upon how you observe it. As a result, they
couldn't decide if light was really waves or made up of
particles.

This is one of the dilemmas that Einstein was able to
resolve by challenging our assumptions about our perceptions of time and space with his celebrated theory of relativity.

As the story goes, the whole thing started from a kind of
daydream that he had when he was sixteen years old during
a math class. He was bored with the class, and ended up
getting a "D" in it. But as he was looking at the window, his
mind wandering, the thought came to him: "What would the
world look like if you were sitting on the end of a light

n?" At first you might consider this to be just a silly, roductive adolescent daydream. But, as we have seen, stein would physically associate himself into his imagiry constructs. He actually put himself onto the beam of ght in his imagination. At one point in this process he imagined holding a mirror out in front of him and wondered f he would see his reflection. Try it yourself. Imagine you are on a light beam hurtling through space holding up a mirror and looking at yourself.

- What would you answer?
- Do you think you would see your reflection or not?

Usually part of the people I ask answer that you would see your reflection and the other part answer you wouldn't see your reflection. (The rest are just confused.)

And right there is the crux of the problem! Based on how we think about it, we will give different answers or no answer at all. Our way of thinking about it has just created a problem. Why do we come up with different answers?

What was Einstein's answer?

At first Einstein reasoned, "From a position off the light beam - if one were sitting on an asteroid floating in space and watching a person go by on the light beam - it would appear that the person on the light beam can't see his reflection. One can clearly observe that the rider is constantly catching up to the light that has left his face - he is moving right along with the light. So he couldn't see himself."

Then he thought, "But if I am the person on the light beam, how do I know that it is not the person on the asteroid who is going at the speed of light in the opposite direction? Why is that person's point of reference more real than mine? How do I know that the point of reference for reality is not me out here on the light beam and that the person on the asteroid is actually the one moving with respect to me? If that's the case, I ought to see my reflection just like I would in any other frame of reference."

So the question arose, "Whose point of view is the real one?"

The observer on the asteroid says, "This is the real frame of reference, and everything moves with respect to me!"

But the rider on the light beam says, "Wait a minute! Why is that little asteroid any more the source of reality than my light beam?"

When you can see it from both points of view, how do you resolve the question? What is the reality about the mirror and the light beam?

Einstein took up the study of physics in an effort to help find a solution to the problem posed by his daydream, but he ran into the same contradictions there. According to the traditional laws of physics, the speed of waves was supposed to depend only on the *medium* and not on the *source* (i.e., sound waves travel at a different speed in water than they do in air regardless of how the sound is made). And waves always travel at the same speed in the same medium regardless of the source. For example, according to wave theory, sound waves from a passing train cover the distance to the observer in the same time no matter how fast the train is moving. Since light was also supposed to be made of waves, the same thing should be true for light. A stationary observer on an asteroid, watching Einstein and his mirror go by, should always see the light leaving Einstein's face at the same speed no matter how fast Einstein was moving. This meant he would catch up to the light leaving his face and his image should disappear.

Yet, on the other hand, Einstein still felt intuitively that his image should not disappear (any more than a person traveling in a jet at the speed of sound should have his voice suddenly disappear). Why should reality be distorted only for the moving observer?

But then on the other hand, if the moving observer's image didn't disappear from the mirror, then the observer on the asteroid should see the light traveling toward the mirror at **twice** its normal speed, and that didn't fit with Einstein's experience or beliefs either.

Classical physics had always viewed the world from the point of view of the stationary observer. No one had actually ever ridden on the end of a light beam - only Einstein, in his imagination.

The fact that constructed images engaged Einstein's kines-thetic system, however, made the question take on a special emotional significance for Einstein. The two visual perspec-tives (one from memory and one from imagination) were both just as real on a feeling level for Einstein. It was not simply a 'mental game' for Einstein, it was a question of 'God' thoughts'. He believed that neither frame of reference should be more real than the other and that light should function normally for both. He attempted to see if there were any way for the speed of light to be the same for both the person holding the mirror and the observer on the asteroid.

In fact, the experimenters Michelson and Morley had already shown that the speed of light stayed the same regardless of whether the speed is measured by an observer in a stationary system or by an observer in a system moving at a constant speed relative to the light source.   But there was no way to understand or explain this result from the existing models of physics.

The solution to the dilemma began to come when Einstein realized that ideas like "speed," "space" and "time" had always been assumed to be fundamental properties of reality that existed independently of the matter that was in them and of the individual who was observing them - such that:

"If matter were to disappear, space and time alone would remain behind (as a kind of stage for physical happening)." [1]

Einstein realized that this was an assumption and not something we could actually know directly, since our experience of 'space' and 'time' always came from patterns derived from sensory perceptions of material objects made by 'observers'. This led him to challenge some of our most basic assumptions about reality.

Challenging Basic Assumptions About 'Space'

According to Einstein:

> *The purpose of mechanics (in physics) is to describe how bodies change their position in space with 'time'.*[2]

This is a statement that most of us would take for granted as being meaningful. But driven by the imaginary dilemma of the light beam, Einstein realized, *"It is not clear what is to be understood here by 'position' and 'space'."*[3] To simplify the dilemma of the light beam, Einstein formulated it in another imaginary construction that is closer to the reality we are used to experiencing:

> *I stand at the window of a railway carriage which is travelling uniformly, and drop a stone on the embankment, without throwing it. Then, disregarding the influence of the air resistance, I see the stone descend in a straight line. A pedestrian who observes the misdeed from the footpath notices that the stone falls to earth in a parabolic curve. I now ask: Do the "positions" traversed by the stone lie "in reality" on a straight line or on a parabola?*[4]

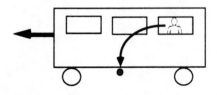

Pedestrian Sees Parabola
With Respect to Embankment

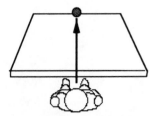

Passenger Sees Straight Line
With Respect to Railway Carriage

Take a moment and think about it. Which way is the stone *really* falling; in a straight line or in a parabola? In which trajectory does the stone fall "in reality?"

Like the person on the asteroid, our first inclination might be to think that the perspective of the pedestrian on the embankment is the 'real' perspective because the Earth is 'bigger' than the train. From this perspective, the stone would "really" fall in a parabola as the pedestrian sees it and the straight line seen by the passenger would be an optical illusion.

But if you were to expand the size of the train car in your imagination to be as big as the earth and passing by it in space, similar differences in perception would still be there; it is just that the confrontation about whose point of reference was being considered would be more obvious. As Einstein once said to a train conductor, "What time does Zurich arrive at this train?"

Einstein realized he could not solve the problem with the same type of thinking that was creating it. Thus far, he had been looking out at the outside world and asking questions about *it*. Einstein decided to turn his exploration inward and ask questions about the 'formal causes' of space and time. Phenomena like "speed," "space" and "time" are 'concepts' or patterns derived from our sensory and psychological perceptions. Einstein pointed out:

> *Science has taken over from pre-scientific thought the concepts of space, time and material object...All these space-like concepts already belong to pre-scientific thought, along with concepts like pain, goal, purpose, etc. from the field of psychology...The physicist seeks to reduce colors and tones to vibration, the physiologist thought and pain to nerve processes, in such a way that the psychical element as such is eliminated from the causal nexus of existence, and thus nowhere occurs as an independent link in the causal associations.*[5]

Einstein realized that it was necessary to recover this missing "link" in the chain of "causal associations." He wondered, *"what is meant here by motion 'in space'?"* Einstein determined that 'motion' could only be perceived 'with respect to' something else. He concluded that there is no such thing as 'motion' except with respect to some 'reference body'. So if we took away both the train and the embankment, then which way would the stone be falling "in reality?" And, what does it fall with respect to? Most people would probably answer that it would fall with respect to "space." But, Einstein wondered, what exactly is that? To answer that question, he had to look more deeply into his own assumptions about the nature of "space."

The psychological origin of the idea of space, or the necessity for it, is far from being so obvious as it may appear to be on the basis of our customary habit of thought...[It] is suggested by certain primitive experiences. Suppose that a box has been constructed. Objects can be arranged in a certain way inside the box, so that it becomes full.

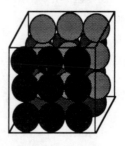

The possibility of such arrangements is a property of the material object "box", something that is given with the box, the "space enclosed" by the box. This is something

which is different for different boxes, something that is thought quite naturally as being independent of whether or not, at any moment, there are any objects in the box, its space appears to be 'empty'.

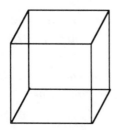

So far, our concept of space has been associated with the box. It turns out, however, that the storage possibilities that make up the box-space are independent of the thickness of the walls of the box. Cannot this thickness be reduced to zero, without the 'space' being lost as a result? The naturalness of such a limiting process is obvious, and now there remains for our thought the space without the box, a self-evident thing, yet it appears to be so unreal if we forget the origin of this concept.[6]

Einstein is saying that we essentially assume 'empty space' is the "storage possibilities" of a box "without the box." Thus, our unconscious presupposition is that the "space" which makes up our "universe" is an immense, unmoving empty box that everything else moves in respect to. If the earth and the train were removed, the stone would fall with respect to this huge, still box.

By uncovering these "primitive" experiences and presuppositions about space, Einstein was then able to question some of these basic assumptions.

*When a smaller box **s** is situated, relatively at rest, inside the hollow space of a larger box **S**, then the hollow space of **s** is a part of the hollow space of **S**, and the same "space", which contains both of them belongs to each of the boxes. When **s** is in motion with respect to **S**, however, the concept is less simple. One is then inclined to think that **s** encloses always the same space, but a variable part of the space **S**. It then becomes necessary to apportion to each box its particular space...and to assume that these two spaces are in motion with respect to each other.*

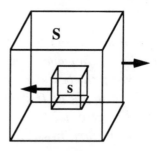

Before one has become aware of this complication, space appears as an unbounded medium or container in which material objects swim around. But it must now be remembered that there is an infinite number of spaces, which are in motion with respect to each other.[7]

According to Einstein, we think of our universe as an "unbounded medium or container in which material objects swim around" - as if God had one large box in which he placed all of the material objects which make up our universe. But as we think about it more deeply, we begin to recognize that this assumption is 'too simple'. When we become aware that there are many potential boxes, we realize there is no one single big **S** space in which the little **s** spaces swim. Rather, big **S** space is the *system of relationships* between all of the little **s** spaces.

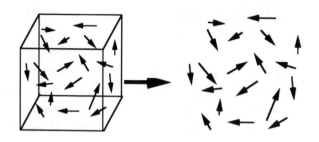

The Universe is Not an 'Unbounded Container', It is the System of Relationships Between an Infinity of Spaces

Einstein concluded, *"we entirely shun the vague word "space," of which, we must honestly acknowledge, we cannot form the slightest conception, and we replace it by "motion relative to a practically rigid body of reference."*

Thus, our rider on the light beam and the observer on the asteroid are not two objects 'swimming around' in 'God's box' - a single large, unmoving empty container - but rather two small **s** spaces, among an infinity of other small **s** spaces, all moving with respect to one another. Similarly, the pedestrian and train passenger are two small **s**'s moving with respect to one another (which are made up of many other small **s**'s moving with respect to each other). And the universe in which they all live; the pedestrian and the passenger, light beam rider and observer, is made up of "an infinite number of spaces, which are in motion with respect to each other."

While this shift in assumptions regarding the basic nature of "space" may not seem that dramatic, its implications are potentially immense. It lead Einstein to reexamine some of our other fundamental concepts about the universe and to find out what other unconscious assumptions were being made.

Challenging Basic Assumptions About 'Simultaneity'

The classical measurement of 'space' depends on the measurer **looking** at where something begins and ends on a measuring implement, such as a ruler. Einstein realized that a fundamental presupposition of making these measurements was that events happen "simultaneously', i.e., that we see the beginning and the end of the object on the ruler at the same time. While this presupposition holds pretty well for our normal (yet limited) perceptions of the world around us, it does not hold very well for very large distances (such as the planets and stars), very small distances (such as the space between atoms), very high speeds (such as the speed of light) or when the two 'spaces' are moving with respect to each other.

Einstein started realizing that most of physics, and most of the ways that people perceive the world, were based on certain presuppositions about measurement. For instance, how would you determine how fast that person on the light beam was going? How do we do it on earth? We take a yardstick or measuring rod and mark where something begins and ends.

But what if the object I was measuring was moving very fast? I might see the left edge of the object at the beginning of the yardstick at time one (t1), but by the time I move my eyes to see where the other end of the object is, it has moved. In other words, if I start measuring by perceiving where one side of the object is in relationship to the yardstick at t1, by the time I even perceive the part of the ruler and the part of the board, and they are in the same place, the board would have moved on. I might measure this board as being only a fraction of its actual size.

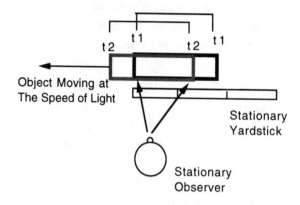

If you were on an asteroid trying to measure something moving at the speed of light (186,000 miles per second) with a yardstick, it could move a substantial distance in the time that it took you to look from one end of the yardstick to the other.

In line with his basic strategy, Einstein formed a symbolic image and began simulating some interactions in an attempt to get a 'clearer picture' of the concept and discover where the assumptions were that were being taken for granted.

*Lightning has struck the rails on our railway embankment in two places **A** and **B** far distant from each other. I make the additional assertion that these two lightning flashes occurred simultaneously. If I ask you whether there is sense in this statement, you will answer my question with a decided "Yes." But if I now approach you with the request to explain to me the sense of the statement more precisely, you find after some consideration that the answer to this question is not so easy as it appears at first sight.*

After some time perhaps the following answer would occur to you: "The significance of the statement is clear in itself and needs no further explanation; of course it would require some consideration if I were to be commissioned to determine by observations whether in the actual case the two events took place simultaneously or not."

*I cannot be satisfied with this answer for the following reason. Supposing that as a result of ingenious considerations an able meteorologist were to discover that the lightning must always strike the places **A** and **B** simultaneously, then we should be faced with the task of testing whether or not this theoretical result is in accordance with reality. We encounter the same difficulty with all physical statements in which the conception "simultaneous" plays a part.*[8]

By formulating the purely fictitious, but symbolically significant, scenario of the *"able meteorologist"* who is able to *"discover that the lightning must always strike the places A and B simultaneously,* Einstein challenges the presupposition that *"the significance of the statement (about simultaneous lightning flashes) is clear in itself and needs no further explanation."* To find the underlying assumptions related to "simultaneity," Einstein goes on to create a specific scenario within his imaginary construction which is an example of the problem.

*After thinking the matter over for some time you then offer the following suggestion with which to test simultaneity. By measuring along the rails, the connecting line **AB** should be measured up and an observer placed at the midpoint **M** of the distance **AB**. This observer should be supplied with an arrangement (e.g. two mirrors inclined at 90°) which allows him to visually observe both places **A** and **B** at the same time. If the observer perceives the two flashes at the same time, then they are simultaneous.*

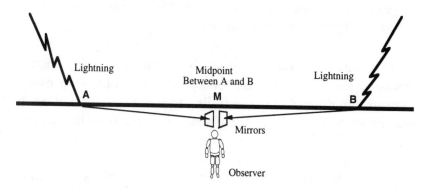

I am very pleased with this suggestion, but for all that I cannot regard the matter as quite settled, because I feel constrained to raise the following objection: "Your definition would certainly be right, if only I knew that the light by means of which the observer at **M** perceives the lightning flashes travels along the length **A—>M** with the same velocity as along the length **B—>M**. But an examination of this supposition would only be possible if we already had at our disposal the means of measuring time. It would thus appear as though we are going in a logical circle."

After further consideration you cast a somewhat disdainful glance at me — and rightfully so — and you declare: "I maintain my previous definition nevertheless, because in reality it assumes absolutely nothing about light. There is only one demand to be made of the definition of simultaneity, namely, that in every real case it must supply us with an empirical decision as to whether or not the conception that has to be defined is fulfilled. That my definition satisfies this demand is indisputable. That light requires the same time to traverse the path **A—>M** as for the path **B—>M** is in reality neither a supposition nor a hypothesis about the physical nature of light, but a stipulation

which I can make of my own free will in order to arrive
at a definition of simultaneity."[9]

It is obvious that Einstein is forming a clear visual construction related to the concept and is identifying every assumption related to it - including that the light traveling in one direction goes at the same speed as light traveling in the other direction.   Through this process he arrives at an underlying assumption that we have to make in order to stay out of the logical circle that "In order to demonstrate that events are simultaneous, we need to presuppose the existence of a way of measuring time, but in order to have a way of measuring time we need to presuppose the existence of simultaneous events." We must stipulate that "simultaneity" means an observer sees two equally distant events happening at once with respect to a midpoint M.

At this stage, Einstein now continues his "combinatory play" by adding different perspectives and movement to his imaginary construction.

Up to now our considerations have referred to a
particular body of reference, which we have styled a
"railway embankment." We suppose a very long train
travelling along the rails with the constant velocity **v**
and in the direction indicated by the figure below.
People traveling in this train will with advantage use
the train as a rigid reference-body; they regard all
events in reference to the train. Then every event which
takes place along the line also takes place at a particular
point of the train. Also the definition of simultaneity
can be given to the train in exactly the same way as
with respect to the embankment. As a natural
consequence, however, the following question arises:

Are two events (e.g. the two strokes of lightening **A** *and*
B*) which are simultaneous with reference to the railway*

embankment also simultaneous relatively to the train?
We shall show directly that the answer must be in the
negative.

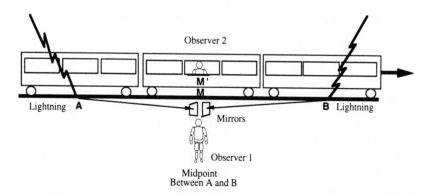

"*When we say that the lightning strokes* ***A*** *and* ***B*** *are*
simultaneous with respect to the embankment, we
mean: the rays of light emitted at the places ***A*** *and* ***B****,*
where the lightning occurs, meet each other at the
midpoint ***M*** *of the length* ***A—>B*** *of the embankment.*
But the events ***A*** *and* ***B*** *also correspond to positions A*
and ***B*** *on the train. Let* ***M'*** *be the midpoint of the*
distance ***A—>B*** *on the travelling train. Just when the*
flashes of light occur (as judged from the embankment),
this point ***M'*** *naturally coincides with point* ***M****, but it*
moves towards the right in the diagram with the
velocity ***v*** *of the train. If an observer sitting in the*
position ***M'*** *in the train did not possess this velocity,*
then he would remain permanently at ***M****, and the light*
rays emitted by the flashes of lightning ***A*** *and* ***B*** *would*
reach him simultaneously, i.e. they would meet just
where he is situated. Now in reality (considered with
respect to the railway embankment) he is hastening
towards the beam of light coming from ***B****, whilst he is*
riding on ahead of the beam of light coming from ***A****.*
Hence the observer will see the beam of light emitted

*from **B** earlier than he will see beam of light emitted from **A**. Observers who take the railway train as their reference-body must therefore come to the conclusion that the lightning flash **B** took place earlier than the lightning flash **A**.*[10]

As he did with the concept of space, Einstein finds the point where the old assumptions break down - based on the definition of 'simultaneity', the same events will not be judged as simultaneous by a moving and stationary observer. The concept is "less simple" than it has been previously treated.

At first we might be inclined to think that the difference in time perception is just an 'optical illusion' on the part of the moving observer. But that presupposes that the location of the observer on the embankment is somehow more special than that of the observer on the train. If the two observers were both on equal sized asteroids observing events in space around them, the discrepancy would still be the same, it would just be more obvious that neither was the 'real' reference point for time. Einstein concludes:

We thus arrive at the important result:

Events which are simultaneous with reference to the embankment are not simultaneous with respect to the train, and vice versa (relativity of simultaneity). Every reference-body has its own particular time; unless we are told the reference-body to which the statement of time refers, there is not meaning in a statement of the time of an event.

Now before the advent of the theory of relativity it had always been tacitly assumed in physics that the statement of time had an absolute significance, i.e., that it is independent of the state of motion of the body of reference. But we have just seen that this assumption is incompatible with the most natural definition of simultaneity.[11]

Einstein's point is that there had always been the unconscious tacit assumption that events in the universe took place inside of an immense, eternally still 'box' that defined 'real' space and 'real' time. Einstein's 'thought experiments', however, lead him to question that assumption. He concluded that God did not make one big box, but rather an infinite number of small boxes all moving with respect to each other and each with "its own particular time."

Challenging Basic Assumptions About 'Time'

Einstein's questions about the assumptions behind the concept of 'simultaneity' and the conclusion that *"every reference body has its own particular time"* brought him to ask other basic questions about the nature of what we call "time" and "objective reality."

What do we mean by rendering objective the concept of time? Let us consider an example. A person A ("I") has the experience "it is lightning". At the same time the person A also experiences such a behavior of the person B as brings the behavior of B into relation with his own experience "it is lightning". Thus it comes about that A associates with B the experience "it is lightning". For the person A the idea arises that other persons also participate in the experience "it is lightning". "It is lightning" is now no longer interpreted as an exclusively personal experience, but as an experience of other persons (or eventually only as a "potential experience"). In this way arises the interpretation that "it is lightning", which originally entered into the consciousness as an "experience", is now also interpreted as an (objective) "event". It is just the sum total of all events that we mean when we speak of the "real external world".

At first sight it seems obvious to assume that a temporal arrangement of events exists which agrees with the temporal arrangement of the experiences. In general and unconsciously this was done, until skeptical minds made themselves felt. [For example, the order of experiences in time obtained by acoustical means can differ from the temporal order gained visually, so that

*one cannot simply identify the time sequence of events
with the time sequences of experiences.]*[12]

Einstein indicates that the concept of 'objective time' is
essentially a function of 'consensual reality'. When two
people share a similar experience, they have a tendency to
believe it is an "objective" event rather than that they are
"sharing a similar perspective and 'reference body'." And, as
Einstein points out, "It is just the sum total of all events that
we mean when we speak of the 'real external world'." [And,
of course, this 'sum total of events' is also the basis of our
social, political, religious and scientific systems.]

While we all may intellectually acknowledge the notion of
'consensual reality' and that there are many different 'subjective' realities, we tend to tacitly assume that there *is* one
'real objective reality' that these subjective realities are more
or less better approximations of. Einstein's implication is
that there are actually many different external 'objective'
realities as well.

According to Einstein we typically assume that the sequence of our sensory experience agrees with the temporal
sequence of events in 'reality'; but that there are, in fact,
discrepancies between our experience of the order of events -
such as seeing a flash of lightning and not hearing the sound
of the thunder for several seconds due to the difference
between the speed of sound and the speed of light.

This line of questioning lead Einstein to turn his attention
inward once again to explore the "formal causes" of time.

*But what about the psychological origin of the concept
of time? This concept is undoubtedly associated with
the fact of "calling to mind", as well as with the
differentiation between sense experiences and the
recollection of these. Of itself it is doubtful whether the
differentiation between sense experience and recollection
(or simple re-presentation) is something psychologically*

directly given to us. Everyone has experienced that he has been in doubt whether he has actually experienced something with his senses or has simply dreamt about it. Probably the ability to discriminate between these alternatives first comes about as the result of an activity of the mind creating order.

An experience is associated with a "recollection", and it is considered as being "earlier" in comparison with "present experiences". This is a conceptual ordering principle for recollected experiences, and the possibility of its accomplishment gives rise to the subjective concept of time, i.e. that concept of time which refers to the arrangement of the experiences of the individual.[13]

Thus, according to Einstein, our subjective experience of time is essentially a function of the arrangement or sequence of our internal representations. When we link or associate experiences with one another, we assume that the experiences which precede the others in our mental sequence occurred "earlier" in time than the recollections which follow them. This equation between 'time' and the linear sequencing of our recollections is probably one of the most basic and unconscious assumptions we make about reality. While the correspondence between our experience of the sequence of events and 'time' seems perfectly reasonable and natural, Einstein wondered if perhaps it didn't say more about ourselves as observers than the objective nature of time. He began to wonder if there were other ways that we could conceptualize time than as a linear sequence.

NLP, has done some extensive research into the different ways in which people subjectively represent time and how they influence the way people perceive and give meaning to events (James & Woodsmall, 1987; Andreas & Andreas, 1987; Dilts, 1987, 1990; Bandler, 1988, 1993). The manner in which people represent past and future, and order events in 'time', will often affect their thoughts, emotions and plans.

Take a moment and notice how you subjectively perceive "time." Think of something that happened a) yesterday, b) last week, c) a year ago. How do you know that one happened a day ago and the other a year ago? How do you represent the 'distance' in time between the different events?

Now, look at a clock and mark what time it is. Look away from the clock and look back again when two and half minutes have elapsed. How do you tell that that much time has elapsed? Do you experience it in a different way than you did when you considered the relationship between the events in the previous question?

In the basic model of NLP, there are two fundamental perspectives one can have with respect to time: perceiving something "in time" or "through time."

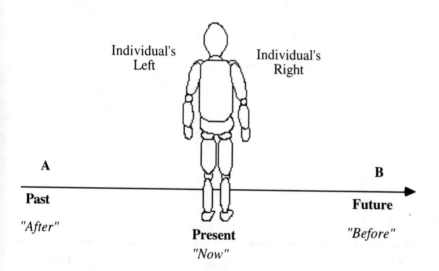

"Through Time" Time Line - Perspective of the Stationary Observer on the Asteroid or Embankment

When one perceives an event "through time" one takes a vantage point that is outside of the sequence of events, disassociated from whatever is being observed or measured - like Einstein's stationary observer on the asteroid watching the rider on the light beam or the pedestrian on the embankment observing the train. From this perspective, the 'time line' is typically viewed such that 'past' and 'future' are lines extending off to the left and right, with the 'now' being somewhere in the middle.

Perceiving an event "in time" involves taking a vantage point associated within the event that is unfolding - like the rider on the light beam or the passenger on the train. From this perceptual position, the 'now' is one's current physical position, with the future represented as a line extending off in the direction one is facing and the past trailing behind - such that one is walking into the future and leaving the past behind.

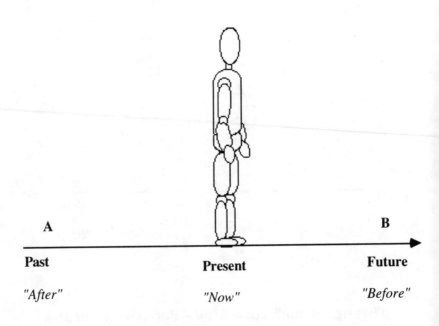

A   B

Past   Present   Future

"After"   *"Now"*   *"Before"*

**"In Time" Time Line - Perspective of the Moving
Observer on the Light Beam or Train**

The two perspectives (which may be represented either visually or through the use of actual physical space) create different perceptions of the same event. Einstein was interested in what different methods of perceiving time would reveal to us, in relation to our maps of the universe. For instance, based on his conclusion that every reference body had its own particular time, he asked, How do we know what time is and how do we measure it? The typical answer is, we look at a clock; a 'through time' perspective that assumes neither we nor the clock is moving. What would happen if we took a different perspective?

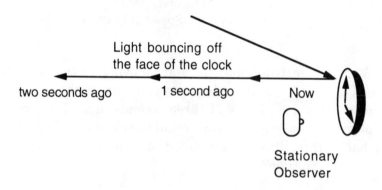

Light bouncing off the face of the clock

two seconds ago   1 second ago   Now

Stationary Observer

Again, Einstein formed a symbolic picture of the process by picturing himself in the tram that he took to work every day when he worked as a patent examiner. The tram passed a large clock in a tower. In the context of this picture, the 'image' of the clock is carried by the light that moves past the observer like water flowing down a river. The image of the clock from one second ago is one hundred and eighty six thousand miles away from the tram passenger by the time the light carrying the image of the movement of the second hand to the next digit arrives.

Einstein wondered what would happen if his tram started moving 'in time' at the speed of light - how would he perceive time if he were looking at the clock? According to his imaginary construction, he should always be keeping up with the light carrying the image of second number one. Time (with respect to the clock) would seem to stand still.

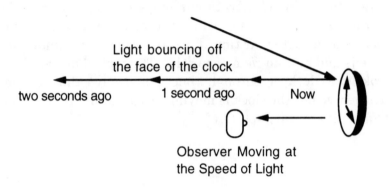

Light bouncing off
the face of the clock

two seconds ago   1 second ago   Now

Observer Moving at
the Speed of Light

What if the tram were to start moving faster than the speed of light? He would begin to catch up on the light that had left the clock two and three seconds ago. Time would appear to go backwards! But would the clock only 'appear' to go backwards Einstein wondered, or would he actually be going back in time?!

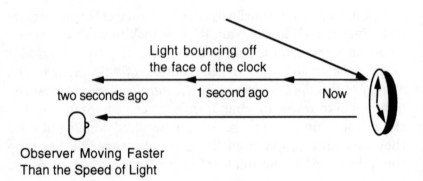

Light bouncing off
the face of the clock

two seconds ago   1 second ago   Now

Observer Moving Faster
Than the Speed of Light

For someone who puts himself into his imaginary constructions, this can be a tricky question! As Einstein reports:

> *"I must confess that at the very beginning when the Special Theory of relativity began to germinate in me, I was visited by all sorts of nervous conflicts. When young I used to go away for weeks in a state of confusion, as one who at that time had yet to overcome the state of stupefacation in his first encounter with such questions."*[14]

Clearly, this was not just a theoretical or mathematical game for Einstein. He wanted to know "God's thoughts." The answer was vital to his sense of reality and identity. The whole of Newtonian reality had been based on presuppositions about **absolute** time and space, but Einstein's combinatory play had lead him to ask some questions that challenged the fundamental nature of time and space. Rather than being 'absolute', time and space were more like God's "thought experiments."

I think it is important to keep in mind at this stage that these questions and conclusions were not simply esoteric musings of an off beat scientist. The changes in assumptions they brought about paved the way for the 'atomic age', space travel and the eventual deaths of tens of thousands of people at Hiroshima and Nagasaki.

Some Implications of Einstein's Theory of Relativity

If you were to look at the night sky and see the moon and some stars, you would most likely presuppose that what you are seeing is all happening at the same time. In reality, the moon is much closer than the stars and the light coming from it has much less distance to travel and therefore reaches our eyes much sooner than the light from the stars. When we sit on our little asteroid and look at the stars at night, we think that what we are seeing is all happening simultaneously. But if you try to measure the distance between one star and another star you are trying to measure the distance between something which might have happened fifty thousand years ago and something which might have happened two thousand years ago.

You are looking at history, you are looking at time, not just space and distance. [It may be somewhat disconcerting to realize that a supernova capable of destroying the Earth may have already happened a thousand years ago, but we do not know it yet because it takes so long for the light carrying that information to travel to the Earth where we can see it and register it. But of course when the light arrives, the problem arrives right along with it!]

Similarly, the sunlight that warms and tans our skin when we are sunbathing is not really from "now" - at least not from the same "now" that we are in when we experience it.

Aristotle had maintained that *"what is bounded by the 'now' is thought to be time"* and suggested that the 'now' was similar to a point on a line in between past and future. In this view, time is like an arrow that moves only in one direction. The past is over forever, the future has not yet happened and the whole universe is in one "now" hurtling into the future. As Einstein pointed out:

> *"[N]ow" loses for the spatially extended world its objective meaning...space and time must be regarded as a four-dimensional continuum that is objectively unresolvable...Since there exist in this four-dimensional structure no longer any sections which represent "now" objectively, the concepts of happening or becoming are indeed not completely suspended, but yet complicated. It appears therefore more natural to think of physical reality as a four-dimensional existence, instead of, as hitherto, the evolution of a three-dimensional existence.*[15]

In Einstein's conception, reality cannot be a single linear "evolution of three dimensional existence" which is the same everywhere in the universe. Our "now" is the future for some parts of the universe and the past for others. In Einstein's four dimensional existence 'past' and 'future' are an ongoing dimension just like 'up' and 'down' or 'left' and 'right'. Time is something that we can potentially travel through in the same way we move through the other three dimensions of reality.

On this little asteroid of ours, we don't usually think about things Einstein's way. Things never move very fast, never go very far in relation to the larger scope of the universe. But when we start dealing with very long or very short time frames and very fast speeds, all of these rules that we use to describe this relatively small piece of reality don't necessarily work in the same way anymore.

And so, what if we return to our two people on an asteroid and a light beam each potentially moving around very quickly with respect to the other? How are they going to measure each other's reality?

According to the old model of the universe:

> *"[P]hysical reality", thought of as being independent of the subjects experiencing it, was conceived as consisting, at least in principle, of space and time on*

one hand, and of permanently existing material points, moving with respect to space and time, on the other. [16]

Speed is generally measured as the distance, or space some "material" object has covered, divided by the time it took to cover that amount of space. The Newtonian way of thinking about it is that time, space and material objects are concrete and real, and speed is an abstraction. Speed is determined by the relationship between time and space with respect to a material object.

But light always goes the same speed no matter what the medium is in which is traveling and no matter how fast the source or the measurer are going. This lead Einstein to turn inward again in order to seek more basic assumptions.

This formation of concepts (i.e., of space and time) already presupposes the concept of material objects (e.g. "boxes")...It appears to me, therefore, that the formation of the concept of material object ("matter") must precede concepts of time and space. [17]

According to Einstein, our psychological perception of both space and time are built on the assumption and presupposition that there are permanent material objects. In other words, our conception of 'space' was derived from our perception of boxes inside of other boxes and our conception of 'time' was a result of our mental ability to recollect sequences of material events. This implies that it is our belief in and perception of 'things' and 'objects' that is the 'epistemological' foundation for our mental models of time and space.

Aristotle pointed out that the same sensory perceptions could either be oriented toward 'things' (the "incidental objects of sense") or toward higher level relationships that he called the "common sensibles." Rather than becoming associated with objects in the outside world, "common sensibles" expressed deeper patterns and relationships that were shared by all of the senses. In a similar way, Einstein sought for the deeper level patterns in the universe - the "common sensibles" within "God's thoughts" - as the basis for his epistemology rather than the material objects.

Instead of matter, Einstein ended up concluding that light itself was the ultimate medium in which everything took place and that the speed of light was the constraint for how fast that reality could unfold. That is, that both perception and reality are a function of electromagnetic energy - light. Einstein's famous equation **E=mc²** is essentially a statement that matter (material objects) is ultimately made of this electromagnetic energy.

If we keep in mind Einstein's earlier statement that *"When...a certain picture turns up in many...series, then - precisely through such return - it becomes an ordering element for such series, in that it connects series which themselves are unconnected,"* we can see that, because the speed of light was always the <u>same</u> no matter what frame of reference it was observed from, light was the ordering element or organizing principle for **all** frames of reference. Light is the water in which all of the observers and the events being observed are swimming.

The implication is that the underlying relationship between events defined by the speed of light is the deeper reality than space, time and even matter. Time, space and 'material objects' are actually the 'abstractions' which are derived from the speed of light, and must change to always preserve that relationship.

From this presupposition, Einstein concluded that since the person on the light beam and the person on the asteroid were in different places and moving with respect to one another, they would experience the **same** event happening in **different ways**. Since space, time and matter were flexible relative to the position of the observer, the material objects within time and space would be flexible too. Thus, the perception and measurement, of space, time and material

objects by the two observers would be altered by the fact that
the electromagnetic field (light) emanating from the event
would not reach them in the same way - just as the pedestrian on the embankment and the train passenger see the
two lightning flashes happening at different times.

This is the core of Einstein's *theory of relativity,* which in
essence postulates that not only the experience of reality but
the form of reality is relative to the frame of reference of the
observer. That is, that natural "laws" are *"covariant with
respect to the arbitrary continuous transformations of the
coordinates"* of the observer and the material objects he or
she is observing.

Thus, the rider on the light beam would see his reflection,
but the observer on the asteroid wouldn't see him going
faster than the speed of light because of the way the light
coming from the person on the light beam would reach him.
Time would be 'dilated' and length would be 'contracted'. The
person on the asteroid would see the fellow on the light beam
moving a much shorter distance and taking a much longer
time to go that distance than the fellow on the light beam
would be measuring from his own frame of reference.

So even though the fellow on the light beam is perceiving
himself going a certain distance at a certain speed within his
own frame of reference, the observer on the asteroid is seeing
him going a different distance in a different amount of time
from his frame of reference. But what **will** be the **same** in
both realities is the relationship defined by the speed of the
light. The person on the asteroid and the person on the light
beam will perceive each other moving different distances in
different times but the **relationship** between the distance
and time will always be the same for both.

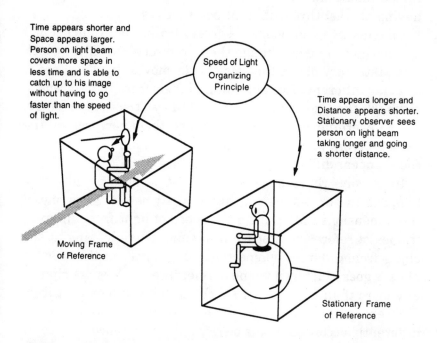

Time appears shorter and Space appears larger. Person on light beam covers more space in less time and is able to catch up to his image without having to go faster than the speed of light.

Speed of Light Organizing Principle

Time appears longer and Distance appears shorter. Stationary observer sees person on light beam taking longer and going a shorter distance.

Moving Frame of Reference

Stationary Frame of Reference

Characteristics of Time, Space and Material Objects Change in Order for the Speed of Light to Remain Constant

Borrowing Einstein's strategy to think about 4-dimensional space with a three dimensional analogy, we can relate Einstein's theory of relativity to the phenomena of foreshortening in visual perspective. The Renaissance in Western Europe occurred largely as a result of the discovery of perspective. If you look at the same object from different angles the object appears to be different sizes. If you look at a building from the front, the sides will appear foreshortened to a degree depending on your angle of view. If you look at the same building from the side, the front will appear foreshortened to a certain degree depending on your angle of the view. In fact, Leonardo da Vinci (the quintessential renaissance man) equated the process of understanding with having at least three different perspectives.

Imagine two stationary observers frozen in 3-dimensional space who can never change their point of view. If they look at a stationary object that also never moves, they will see it as being different sizes according to their frame of reference - although the size of the object itself doesn't actually change. If they were never allowed to change their perspective, the two observers would never know that the length of the object could appear differently to someone else.

In a way, Einstein is saying that something like this happens in our 4-dimensional world - where time is one of the dimensions. Measuring the speed of light from different frames of reference in space **and** time is like looking at the object from different perspectives. Light goes at the speed it always goes in its own frame of reference - it does not change any more than a block of wood changes if you look at it from different points of view. It is just that viewer sees it differently according to his own frame of reference.

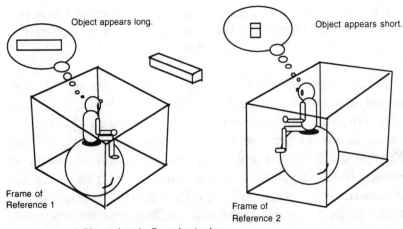

Object appears long.

Object appears short.

Frame of Reference 1

Frame of Reference 2

3-Dimensional Foreshortening

Analogy of 3-Dimensional 'Foreshortening' With Respect to Two Stationary Observers

As a result of the understanding of depth and perspective and the other ideas that blossomed as a result of the renaissance, we also realized that the Earth was not the center of the solar system, and that the sun and other planets did revolve around the universe. Einstein's theory of relativity extended that notion to an even deeper level of reality. Our universe does not exist inside of a single immense container defining absolute space and time. There is no single 'God's box' which serves as the ultimate frame of reference events in the universe. We certainly cannot assume that the whole rest of the universe moves with respect to our tiny frame of reference. We need to expand our model of the universe to cover a multitude of perspectives and realities.

Another analogy for constancy of the speed of light might be derived from exploring how we would see a three dimensional object from the frame of reference of Einstein's two dimensional beings in their flat world. Imagine for a moment that you are one of these beings and a bubble suddenly floats through your world. What would you see?

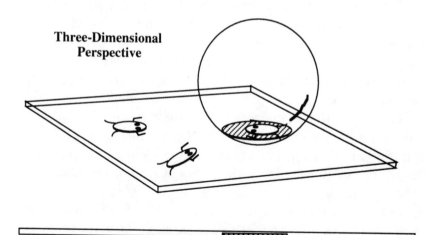

Two-Dimensional Beings Viewing a Bubble

If you are distant from the place where the bubble inter-sects your world you will see a curved line that first grows bigger and then small again and disappears. If the bubble intersects where you are located, you will suddenly be surrounded on all sides by an ever widening circle, which will eventually begin to shrink again and disappear.

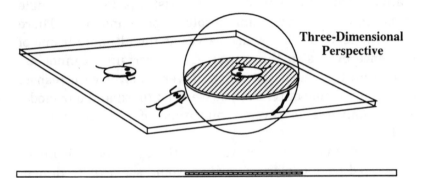

Three-Dimensional Perspective

Two-Dimensional Perspective

A Bubble Appears Like a Circle in the Flat World

If the bubble stops moving, the distant observers will be able to examine it, move around it and inside of it and eventually conclude that the object is a particular sized circle. If the bubble begins to move again, our two dimen-sional beings will suddenly begin to see the circle 'magically' getting bigger or smaller. They would believe that the phenomenon that they were observing was a circle that was changing its size with respect to them. They would have to jump to another level altogether to realize that the phenom-enon was in fact a sphere that always stayed the same size and they were just seeing different aspects of it.

But even from the 2-dimensional frames of reference, what will stay the same, no matter which angle or place that the sphere intersects their flat world, is that they will perceive a circle - which could be defined mathematically by the equation $2\pi r$. "Pi" (π) is a constant that defines the **relationship** needed to make the circle and the sphere.

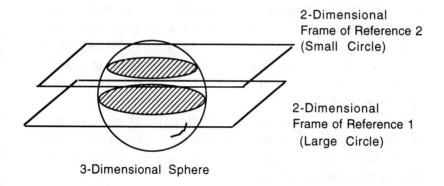

2-Dimensional
Frame of Reference 2
(Small Circle)

2-Dimensional
Frame of Reference 1
(Large Circle)

3-Dimensional Sphere

By analogy, when we try to measure a 4-dimensional world with our 3-dimensional frame of reference, we are seeing something similar to slices of a 4-dimensional "sphere" with our 3-dimensional plane. We cannot see the whole sphere, but the speed of light "c" is like "π" in the 2-dimensional frame of reference. It gives us information about the key relationship that is needed to make up the 4-dimensional reality we are trying to perceive.

In summary, while the nature of reality is relative to each person, neither reality nor one's perception of it is simply arbitrary. Thus, if a person on a light beam holding a mirror passed a person on an asteroid, the person with the mirror could experience the light traveling a certain distance in a certain time to give the proper speed of light, while the person on the asteroid could experience the light traveling a *different distance* in a *different amount of time* in such a way that it would give the *same speed of light* for both. The two frames of reference are connected, not by space or time, but by a relationship defined by the speed of light.

For Einstein, reality wasn't determined by the image, but by the light that produces the image. Einstein believed the speed at which light propagated through our universe was the most absolute and concrete organizing principle, and that our experience of space and time had to adjust in order to keep that speed the same. In other words, the relationship defined by the speed of light was more real and constant than the actual physical measurement or expression of events in space and time - i.e., this *relationship was more constant and real than material objects.*

Isaac Newton had described all natural phenomena as events occurring in the framework of absolute space and time. Einstein described time and space as events occurring within the framework of light.

The Strategy Behind the Theory of Relativity

While the theory of relativity is one of Einstein's key contributions to the world, and is interesting and fascinating in and of itself, the content of the theory is not what is most important to this study. Our interest is in the thought process behind Einstein's theories.

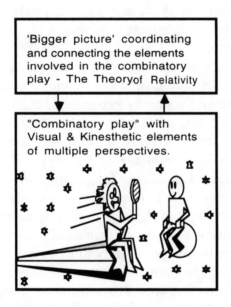

'Bigger picture' coordinating and connecting the elements involved in the combinatory play - The Theory of Relativity

"Combinatory play" with Visual & Kinesthetic elements of multiple perspectives.

Einstein's Two-Level Macro Strategy

In many ways, it is easy to see the multi-level macro-strategy, that we identified in chapter 3, at work in the thought process that lead to the theory of relativity. The visual and kinesthetic sensations of the two observers on the light beam and the asteroid, the pedestrian and the train passenger, or the tram rider are the elements involved in the "combinatory play." The perceptions of the moving and stationary observers are flexible and relative. But in the larger 'visual survey' at the higher level, the relationship between these elements is stable and well defined enough that it can be connected to logical, verbal and mathematical models.

At the level of micro strategy, picturing oneself on a light beam from multiple perspectives is a very different type of thinking than thinking in mathematical symbols. In fact, Einstein didn't invent the equation to describe relativity, he used an equation* that already existed in the field of pure mathematics as the language to express what he saw and felt in his imagination.

Einstein's form of imaging doesn't require extensive training in physics. Instead it requires a vivid, active imagination that organizes and connects experiences together in a particular strategy. An adolescent (as Einstein was when the image first occurred to him) or even a child without any training in physics could create this type of imagery. To Einstein, this type of visual fantasizing was an essential element of science. It allowed one to operate at a level of perception that could synthesize and unify seemingly opposing or antagonistic concepts or frames of reference by identifying unconscious, and potentially limiting assumptions.

Einstein developed the strategy to identify and challenge basic assumptions and then synthesize seemingly conflicting perspectives to a very high degree. The establishment of the four-dimensional *space-time continuum* between the moving and stationary observers in the theory of relativity is a perfect example of his ability to widen his map and shift to another level of perspective in order to unify the seemingly incompatible points of view of the moving and stationary observers.

---

* The mathematical equation Einstein used to describe relativity (the Lorentz transformation) is basically an equation describing the change in relationship that happens between one frame of reference and another. The thing that stays constant on both sides of the equation is the speed of light.

In fact, all of Einstein's major discoveries and contributions came from his ability to show the interconnections between two seemingly incompatible systems:

a. This interrelation of different systems was the basis for Einstein's famous $E=mc^2$ equation - which states the relationship between *matter* (which is stationary and solid) and *energy* (which is always changing and moving). Einstein held that *matter was actually a form of energy,* and that *energy was a form of matter,* and that their interrelationship was expressed by the equation $E=mc^2$; where **E**=energy, **m**=mass, and **c**= the speed of light.*

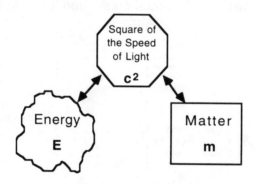

Relationship Between Matter and Energy

b. Einstein won the **Nobel prize** for showing that light had the properties of both a *particle* (which is stationary and solid) and a *wave* (which is continually

---

*Another expression of the same equation would be **E/c=mc**. In other words, energy divided by the speed of light is the same as mass times the speed of light. According to this relationship, when a minuscule amount of mass is annihilated, it is replaced by an immense amount of energy. This, of course, is the principle behind atomic power.

changing and moving). He held that particles were actually 'packets' of waves (or "quanta") and that, when condensed into such packets, waves had the same properties as particles. This is the basis of *quantum theory* in modern physics.

c. Einstein's visualizations regarding *spherical geometry* (the two-dimensional beings in a flat world and his four-dimensional shadows) showed the interrelationship between *three-dimensional* (solid) and *four-dimensional* (changing) systems.

d. Einstein's "thought experiment" involving the man in the elevator pulled through space, unified the concepts the 'gravitational mass' and 'inertial mass'.

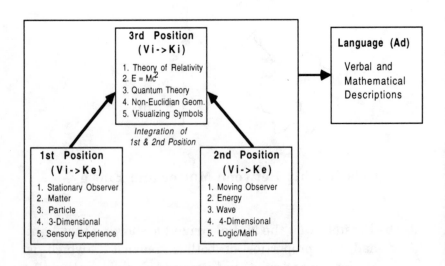

Einstein's Process of Integrating Seemingly Incompatible Perspectives

We can see that *all these discoveries share a similar structure* - a structure that is a direct function of Einstein's basic underlying thinking strategy. This strategy involves integrating at a higher level two fundamentally different perspectives at a lower level. As Einstein put it himself, *"Our thinking creates problems which the same level of thinking can't solve."* To solve the problems one level of thinking has created, we have to move to another level.

Einstein's overall strategy was to solve a problem by finding a way of thinking that is different from the 'kind of thinking which is creating the problem'. The following steps summarize the process that he used over and over again to identify and challenge basic assumptions associated with "space," "simultaneity," "time," etc.:

1) Einstein begins with a paradox that is not satisfactorily explainable or manageable by the existing models - *e.g.* the dilemma relating to the perceptions of the person on the light beam and the observer on the asteroid. (In other words, he finds the place where the current model has made things "too simple.")

2) He states the current model of the problem and finds verbal terms that stands for concepts which are typically taken for granted and questions the parts of the statement which seem to have the most assumptions - *e.g.* (a) *"The purpose of mechanics (in physics) is to 'describe how bodies change their position in space with 'time'."* But, *"It is not clear what is to be understood here by 'position' and 'space'."* (b) *"Is there any sense in this statement 'two lightning flashes occurred simultaneously'?'* (c) *"What do we mean by rendering objective the concept of time?"*

3) He then forms a number of simple symbolic or metaphoric images representing that concept - *e.g.* (a) a train moving with respect to an embankment, (b) lightning bolts striking a train track, or (c) a tram that can travel at the speed of light.

4) He tries to simulate some interaction relating to the problem within his imaginary construct and 'see' the functioning of the 'concept' as clearly as possible by putting himself into different perspectives within his imaginary scenario - *e.g.* (a) the commuter and the pedestrian watching a falling stone, (b) an "able meteorologist" trying to measure simultaneous lightning flashes, or (c) a tram rider watching a clock as he hurtles away from it at the speed of light.

5) Through this "combinatory play" of images and feelings, Einstein finds the place where the old assumption breaks down and *"the concept is less simple."* - *e.g.* (a) *Do the "positions" traversed by the stone lie "in reality" on a straight line or on a parabola? Moreover, what is meant here by motion "in space"?* (b) *"Does the light by means of which the observer at M perceives the lightning flashes travel along the length A—>M with the same velocity as along the length B—>M?* (c) Does the tram rider catch up to the image of the clock and see time 'stand still'?

6) He forms a new assumption based on his combinatory play with his imaginary construction - *e.g.* (a) The assumption of 'independent space' is replaced by the assumption of *"an infinite number of spaces, which are in motion with respect to each other."* (b) The assumption of simultaneity is re-

placed with the assumption that *"events which are simultaneous with reference to the embankment are not simultaneous with respect to the train."* (c) The assumption of absolute time is replaced with the assumption that *" 'now' loses for the spatially extended world its objective meaning."*

7) Working from the new assumption he finds out what *relationship* stays the *same* from all perspectives in his combinatory play - *e.g.* (a) 'motion' and 'trajectory' are perceived *"relative to a particular body of reference."* (b) *"Every reference-body has its own particular time."* (c) *"Space and time must be regarded as a four-dimensional continuum that is objectively unresolvable."*

8) Einstein verbally forms a new concept based on the new assumption that once again makes everything "as simple as possible" - *e.g.* (a) *"We entirely shun the vague word "space," ...and we replace it by "motion relative to a practically rigid body of reference."* (b) *"Unless we are told the reference-body to which the statement of time refers, there is not meaning in a statement of the time of an event."* (c) *"It appears therefore more natural to think of physical reality as a four-dimensional existence, instead of, as hitherto, the evolution of a three-dimensional existence."*

As we can see, questioning one assumption leads to the necessity of questioning another and another. Einstein's exploration of the validity of the assumptions behind the perception of "motion" lead him to challenge basic assumptions about "space." His changes in assumptions about space lead him to question the concept of "simultaneity." His conclusions about the relativity of simultaneity brought him to reconsider presuppositions behind the notion of "objective events." His discoveries of discrepancies in 'objectivity' lead him to question the nature of time, and finally of material objects and matter itself.

Concept	Einstein's Conclusion
motion	There is no absolute 'motion', there is only motion relative to other objects in space.
space	There is no absolute 'space', there are an infinite number of spaces moving relative to each other.
simultaneity	There is no absolute 'simultaneity', there is only simultaneity relative to the position of the observer.
objective events	There are no absolute 'objective events', there are perceptions of events that correspond with the perceptions of others.
time	There is no absolute 'time', every reference body has its own particular time.
material objects	There are no 'permanent material objects', matter is a transformation of electromagnetic energy (light).

As Einstein explained:

Why is it necessary to drag down from the Olympian fields of Plato the fundamental ideas of thought in natural science, and to attempt to reveal their earthly lineage? Answer: In order to free these ideas from the taboo attached to them, and thus to achieve greater freedom in the formation of ideas or concepts...

In the previous paragraphs we have attempted to describe how the concepts of space, time and event can be put psychologically into relation with experiences. Considered logically, they are free creations of the human intelligence, tools of thought, which are to serve the purpose of bringing experiences in relation with each other, so that in this way they can be better surveyed. The attempt to become conscious of the empirical sources of these fundamental concepts should show to what extent we are actually bound to these concepts. In this way we become aware of our freedom, of which, in case of necessity, it is always a difficult matter to make sensible use.[18]

Footnotes to Chapter 6

1. Albert Einstein, *Relativity,* Crown Publishers, Inc., New York, NY, 1961, p. 144.

2. Ibid, p. 9.

3. Ibid, p. 9.

4. Ibid, p. 9.

5. Ibid, pp. 141-142.

6. Ibid, pp. 136-137.

7. Ibid, pp. 138-139.

8. Ibid, pp. 21-22.

9. Ibid, pp. 22-23.

10. Ibid, pp. 25-26.

11. Ibid, pp. 26-27.

12. Ibid, pp. 139-140.

13. Ibid, p. 139.

14. J. Schwartz & M. McGuinness, *Einstein For Beginners,* Pantheon Books, New York, New York, 1983, p. 82.

15. Albert Einstein, *Relativity,* Crown Publishers, Inc., New York, NY, 1961, pp. 149-150.

16. Ibid, p. 144.

17. Ibid, p. 141.

18. Ibid, pp. 141-142.

Chapter 7

Some Psychological Implications of the Theory of Relativity

Ever since it was first formulated, Einstein's theory of relativity has fascinated laymen as much as it has physicists. Certainly, Einstein's realizations about the relative nature of reality apply to more than physics. They also apply to our belief systems and psychological models of the world. Our perceptions and beliefs about the world are subject to change relative to other influences.* Einstein seemed to understand this type of perceptual relativity quite well when he pointed out:

> "If relativity is proved right the Germans will call me a German, the Swiss will call me a Swiss citizen, and the French will call me a great scientist.

> "If relativity is proved wrong the French will call me a Swiss, the Swiss will call me a German, and the Germans will call me a Jew."[1]

---

* There is a clever joke about Einstein's theory of relativity applied to family systems that goes: "When the relatives come over for a visit, space becomes much smaller and time becomes much longer."

A particular behavior or event can be perceived and interpreted in a number of different ways depending upon the frame of reference from which it is viewed. Much of our behavior is influenced and determined by how we perceive ourselves in relationship to others, both from our own point of view and from how we imagine they see us. Einstein's moving and stationary observers provide a classic example of opposing points of view.

In fact, almost every area of science and philosophy has a similar dualism between opposing frameworks at its base. Some examples include:

First Position	Second Position
Stationary Observer	*Moving Observer*
Matter	*Energy*
Particle	*Wave*
3-Dimensional	*4-Dimensional*
Existing Knowledge	*Imagination*
Stable-Solid	*Changing-Moving*
Deviation Reducing	*Deviation Amplifying*
Inhibitory	*Excitatory*
Flesh	*Spirit*
Body	*Mind*
Ego (Reality Principle)	*Id (Pleasure Principle)*
Left Brain	*Right Brain*
Digital	*Analog*
Old	*New*
Parent	*Child*
Critic	*Dreamer*

Such a fundamental pattern may tell us as much about the nature and neurology of the observers that make these models of the world as it does about the actual nature of the world itself. It relates to what Aristotle referred to as "formal causes." In order to act in the world (whether it be riding a bicycle, solving a math equation or building an atomic bomb) human beings must respond to the maps of the world that are created by and stored in their nervous systems. Thus, those models which are the most effective are those which most naturally mirror the way the nervous system is designed. Thought of in this way, the issues dealt with in Einstein's theory of relativity may be a metaphorical way of describing how our nervous systems function as much as it is a description of how the world around us functions.

In NLP, Einstein's two perspectives (the light beam and the asteroid) relate to two very fundamental perceptual frameworks called *'first position'* and *'second position'* (DeLozier & Grinder, 1987). 'First position' involves seeing, hearing and feeling a particular event from one's own perspective. 'Second position' involves seeing, hearing and feeling the same event (including oneself) from the perspective of another person. Obviously, first and second position may also be opposing frames of reference from different belief systems regarding a particular change one is about to make. This provides what is called a *'double description'* of the event. This 'double description' gives us important information that may be left out of any one perspective.

We perceive depth, for example, because our two eyes actually register slightly different images of the same event. The depth that we see is a result of the relationship between these slight differences. In the same way that we presuppose that events happen simultaneously, we are not usually consciously aware of the two different images that our eyes are registering, and only perceive one object when we look at something.

In order to recognize and describe the relationship between two such perspectives we must get **outside** the relationship by shifting up a level to what is called *'third position'* or *'meta-position'* - a perspective **above** 'first' and 'second' position in which one can actually look at the relationship between the two of them. It is from third position that we can actually begin to resolve the conflict and integrate the opposing frames of reference. It is from this position that Einstein was able to see that the perceptions of the moving and stationary observers were actually a manifestation of the same relationship - the relationship defined by the speed of light.

If we look at the dilemma that lead Einstein to his theory of relativity as a metaphor for Einstein's own transition to adulthood (he was twenty six when he formulated the special theory of relativity) some important psychological implications of his theory emerge. Remember that when Einstein first began to become aware of and confront the paradox of the moving and stationary points of reference he was sixteen, an age when most people begin to think about establishing an identity of their own. Consider the metaphorical implications of looking at yourself in a mirror. One interpretation of Einstein's adolescent musings might be, if you use your imagination then you start changing, you think differently from the others around you; but do you still have a self-image?

It is as if the person on the asteroid were saying, "If you start thinking differently, you will lose your identity. I keep mine, but you'll lose sight of your true identity. That's dangerous. You'd better stop thinking that way." The observer on the little asteroid thinks the person flying on the light beam is a daydream, it is all just fantasy. But is it? Or is it only because this individual on the asteroid is so limited in his thinking and lives in such a tiny world view that he can't incorporate the scope of this other world view. Perhaps the observer thinks that the whole universe centers around his little asteroid and the tiny part of the universe that he can see.

The stationary observer can be associated with traditional reality - which involved a stable framework for perceiving a reality made of solid objects with definite measurements, logically related in linear time. The moving observer is associated with creative imagination, a flexible reality, free thinking and change.

Each of Einstein's other major discoveries (all of which he published in his twenty-sixth year - 1905) also involved the integration of similar frameworks - matter and energy, particles and waves, etc. Obviously, these discoveries represented a change in **conceiving** the world around us not a change in actual external reality. Perhaps Einstein's synthesis of the dualism expressed by opposing frames of reference represented a synthesis in his own personality as much as the science of physics. Clearly, Einstein had initially placed himself in the reality of the changing light beam. Afterward, he tried to reconcile the new frame of reference with the traditional perceptions of reality.

Considered in this light, Einstein's theory of relativity can be seen as a basic metaphor for change within a system; and his strategy as a general problem solving strategy for managing resistances related to changing systems. In almost every situation of social or personal change there is a conflict between (1) a part of the system that wants to change, can imagine those changes and believes it is possible, and (2) a part of the system that believes the change is risky, foolish or impossible and is based on an earlier and more limited, but a more stable and familiar, model of the world.

The part that wants to change and establish a new reality is like the moving observer. The part that doesn't believe it is possible, or wants to remain the same is like the stationary observer. And the conflict between the two can be quite severe and limiting. Freud's concept of the eternal conflict between the ego with its stabilizing but repressive 'reality principle' and the id with the driving force of its 'pleasure principle' is remarkably similar in some respects to Einstein's two frames of reference.

Thought of as a metaphor for change, the issue of whether or not the moving observer would see his reflection in the mirror takes on an interesting dimension. As I proposed earlier, the reflection in the mirror can be thought of as one's self image. That is, our perception of our identity. The stationary observer initially believes the moving observer will not see his own image while he is riding on the light beam - i.e., will lose his identity if he is changing. The person on the light beam, however, believes his world will still function perfectly normally.

To find his resolution, Einstein first had to be able to view the universe equally well from each point of view, and maintain the belief that they were not antagonistic. Many people are stuck primarily in one frame of reference, or believe that the frames of reference they are holding are so antithetical to one another that there is no way to reconcile them.

In working to help human systems change, one can borrow many elements from Einstein's strategy in order to 1) help them to fully acknowledge and experience all of the relevant frames of reference, 2) search for any limiting beliefs or unconscious assumptions that may support antagonism between the frames of reference, 3) examine and creatively challenge the presuppositions which hold the limiting assumption in place by moving to another level of thinking.

As an example with respect to human behavior, I was once asked by a mental health facility to help assist a woman who was in a very deep crisis. Her marriage had recently broken up, and as a result, she had become depressed to the point of being suicidal. She was a nurse, and one day she got so depressed she had brought poison home from the hospital where she worked and had planned to kill herself and her three children. Fortunately, she stopped herself from going through with the plan and sought counseling. She was clearly in a desperate state.

She came in and said, "I need to do something, anything to change my state. I need help. I can't stand it anymore."

My first response was to say, "OK, since you want to get out of this negative state, let's start thinking of resourceful reference experiences. Can you recall a positive experience from your past?"

"I don't have any," she replied, "All of my memories are bad and painful."

My initial thought was, "Uh-oh! What shall I do next? She doesn't have any good experiences!" Challenging my own assumptions, I decided to pursue a different direction, telling her, "Well, if you don't have any in the past we'll make something up. We will create a resourceful vision of your future. The main issue is that you can't stand the negative feelings you're trapped in now, so instead of going into the past, let's go to the future and begin to create something that will be a resourceful experience."

I asked her to look up and to the right (the eye accessing cue for constructing visual images in the NLP model) and imagine how she would like things to be. I was pleased to observe that she visibly started to shift her physiology indicating a positive change in her state. Then, she suddenly stopped and returned to her previous state of depression.

I asked, "What happened? Did you stumble onto something negative? Did you hit a block?"

She said, "No."

So I said, "But it seemed like it was working - it seemed to me that you were getting some response. Were you starting to feel better?"

- "Yes."

- "Then why did you stop?"

- "Because it felt funny to put my eyes up there. It was unfamiliar."

What struck me like a lightning bolt was that this person had felt so bad she was going to kill herself and her children. She claimed she was desperate to do anything to make herself feel better. Yet, she stopped doing something that she herself reported was making her feel better because "it felt funny to put my eyes up there." It seemed as if she was saying, "Sorry, I'd rather feel like killing my children than have to do something a little unfamiliar like putting my eyes up and think of the future in order to feel good." My goal was to help "free her from the prison" of her own model of the world by helping her widen her map.

Applying the first step of Einstein's strategy (as outlined in the previous chapter) I put myself in her position and realized the real paradox she was stuck in from within her frame of reference, "My past is lousy, my present is unbearable and the future is unfamiliar and insecure." What emerged from this perspective was the assumption that the universe was not a friendly place. And when the universe is an "unfriendly place" there's nowhere one can go to hide or escape from it.

I began to widen my own map of the situation and think of a way out of the dilemma that involved a different way of thinking than was creating the problem. As with Einstein's dilemma, the first step toward a solution was to identify and acknowledge the two opposing frames of reference in order to reach a "third position" or "meta position" to the perspectives in conflict. She clearly had two 'parts' of herself in conflict - one that wanted to change and one that was afraid to do anything "unfamiliar." The part that wanted to change couldn't stand the past and present, but the other part of her was afraid of the future. She confirmed that this was indeed the "double bind" that she was in - she was afraid of what would happen if she didn't change, but she was even more afraid of what would happen if she did.

In line with the next step in Einstein's strategy, I asked her to form a simple symbolic image of each part. On the one hand, she saw the part of her that wanted to change as a butterfly trying to hatch out of a cocoon; potentially beautiful, but fragile and delicate. On the other hand she pictured a mother Tyrannosaurus Rex with a nest of eggs. The dinosaur knew it was going to become extinct and was afraid of what the future had in store. It felt that it would be better to destroy its nest of eggs than subject them to potential horrors of the future.

_____	**The Elusive Obvious**	$20.00
	Moshe Feldenkrais (hardcover)	
_____	**Patterns of Hypnotic Techniques of Milton H. Erickson, M.D. - Volume I**	$14.95
	Bandler and Grinder (paper)	
_____	**Patterns of Hypnotic Techniques of Milton H. Erickson, M.D. - Volume II**	$17.95
	Bandler, DeLozier, Grinder (hardcover)	
_____	**Provocative Therapy**	$14.00
	Farrelly & Brandsma (hardcover)	
_____	**Practical Magic**	$12.95
	Stephen R. Lankton (paper)	
_____	**Therapeutic Metaphors**	$14.95
	David Gordon (paper)	
_____	**The Wild Days: NLP from 1972 to 1989**	$12.00
	Terry McClendon (paper)	

ORDER FORM   FAX WITH MASTERCARD/VISA OR MAIL THIS CARD TO:

Meta Publications Inc.
P. 0. Box 1910, Capitola, CA 95010
(408) 464-0254 Fax (408) 464-0517

Please send me copies of the books ordered

Subtotal	_____
Tax (add 8% for California residents)	_____
Freight & Handling	4.00
TOTAL AMOUNT ENCLOSED	$ _____

Name _____

Address _____

City_____ State _____ Zip _____

Charge to my credit card: ☐ Visa ☐ MasterCard

  # _____ Exp. Date _____

Signature _____
      (Credit Card Only)

BOOK LIST

Quantity

_____ **Effective Presentation Skills** $22.95
Robert Dilts (hardcover)

_____ **Time for a Change** $19.95
Richard Bandler (hardcover)

_____ **Skills for the Future** $24.95
Robert Dilts (hardcover)

_____ **Magic in Action – Revised** $19.95
Richard Bandler (hardcover)

_____ **The Adventures of Anybody** $12.95
Richard Bandler (hardcover)

_____ **Tools for Dreamers** $24.95
Dilts , Epstien & Dilts (hardcover)

_____ **Changing Belief Systems with NLP** $22.00
Robert Dilts (hardcover)

_____ **No Experience Necessary** $12.95
Scott Nelson (paper)

_____ **Beyond Selling** $19.95
Dan S. Bagley & Edward J. Reese (hardcover)

_____ **Time Line Therapy** $22.95
Tad James & Wyatt Woodsmall (hardcover)

_____ **The Magic of Rapport** $14.00
Jerry Richardson (paper)

_____ **An Insider's Guide To Submodalities** $12.95
Richard Bandler & Will MacDonald (paper)

_____ **The Master Moves** $14.95
Moshe Feldenkrais (paper)

_____ **Roots of Neuro-Linguistic Programming** $22.00
Robert Dilts (hardcover)

_____ **Applications of Neuro-Linguistic Programming** $22.00
Robert Dilts (hardcover)

_____ **Meta-Cation: Prescriptions for Some
Ailing Educational Processes** $12.00
Sid Jacobson (hardcover)

_____ **Phoenix—Therapeutic Patterns of Milton H. Erickson** $14.00
D. Gordon & M. Myers-Anderson (paper)

_____ **Neuro-Linguistic Programming** $24.00
Dilts, Grinder, Bandler et al Limited Edition (hardcover)

(See other side for more books and order form.)

I asked her to take some time and become familiar with each perspective, as Einstein would have done; moving back and forth between the two perspectives and considering one another from each point of view.

The next step was to address the underlying assumption that the universe was "unfriendly." I asked the woman to find the "positive intention" or purpose of each of the two parts of herself. It was a question that she had never considered before and it took her by surprise to think that there could be something "positive" behind her pain and conflict.

After some coaching on my part, she realized that the positive intention of the part of her, represented by the butterfly, that wanted change was "growth." The positive intention of the dinosaur who was afraid of change was "survival" but also "protection" from pain. These were clearly outcomes on the level of values.

To find the new assumption that would unite both frames of reference, I asked her to think of what 'mission' both parts and positive intentions served with respect to her larger 'identity'; i.e., what they were both trying to do positively for her as a person. After some exploration, she concluded that they were both trying to help her be a "successful human being." They just had different values. However, as opposed to the way the problem was initially perceived, by recognizing the positive intentions of the parts, these values no longer seem like polar opposites that were mutually exclusive like 'change' versus 'rigidity'. "Growth" and "survival" were in fact necessary conditions for one another. If one does not protect oneself and survive, one certainly cannot grow. And if one does not grow, one is not likely to survive or be able to protect oneself under changing circumstances (as is indicated by the law of requisite variety).

Working from the new assumption that what was the "same" for both perspectives was the consensus about their common mission of becoming a "successful human being," we reexamined the specific capabilities associated with each part. The "butterfly" part that desired "growth" and change had the ability to "prepare for the future." The "dinosaur" part that wanted "survival" and "protection" had the ability to "assess the present for potential danger." She discovered that not only were these capabilities not in conflict, they were actually quite complementary. Each part could use the capabilities of the other part in order to more successfully fulfill its own values and achieve the common mission. "Preparing for the future" was an important resource for survival and protection as well as growth. "Assessing the present," was just as necessary for growth and change as it was for survival and protection.

The remaining step in helping the woman now was in checking which other assumptions might need to be challenged or reevaluated. The initial stumbling block had been related to the word "familiar." So I decided to check out the assumptions and presuppositions ("formal causes") the woman had associated with "familiarity." I asked, "How would you know if it *was* familiar to put your eyes up and picture a positive future?"

She thought about it for a moment and responded, "I would have done it before I guess."

So I asked "How many times would you have to have done it in order for it to be familiar?"

Seeming a bit confused she said, "I don't know."

I asked her to focus on the bad feeling that she had associated with things that were unfamiliar and trace it back in time to the situations in which she had first felt it (what Aristotle would call the "antecedent causes"). To do this I had her physically put herself "in time" on a time line on the floor representing her personal history and then walk backwards (as one might do in Einstein's four dimensional space-time continuum). She did not consciously know the source of the feeling initially, but as she slowly walked back she began to remember a childhood event that suddenly seemed as fresh as if it had happened only the day before.

She recalled a time in her life when she was a child and had great expectations about her future. In fact, she had constructed very elaborate and clear pictures about how the future would be. For reasons outside of her control, the future she had envisioned never materialized and she was crushed. (As my colleague Richard Bandler says, "Disappointment requires adequate planning.") She had made a vow at that time that she would never set herself up to be hurt in that way again. Her belief was that it was better to have no hope at all then to have false hope.

Her recent break up with her husband had retriggered the feelings associated with these childhood memories and beliefs, causing her to completely shut down any visualization of the future for fear of even deeper disappointment. The problem was, she saw no future whatsoever, which, in turn, served to deepen her depression - another "double bind." She felt "damned if she did, and damned if she didn't."

Once she was aware of these memories, I helped her to sort them out in time. The events she was recalling had happened a long time ago when she did not have the resources and capabilities which she had today. We decided to conduct a "thought experiment" in which she could travel across time on Einstein's light beam or tram and revisit those past experiences with the knowledge and wisdom she possessed as an adult. In particular she could bring the complementary resources of the two parts of herself. In addition to the ability to imagine the future, she was to bring the abilities to "prepare for the future' and to "assess the present." She realized that, with these abilities, the past experience would have been very different. After she had imagined how her responses to a number of the most significant events would have changed, she "returned to the future" deep in thought.

I then talked to her about how it was sometimes possible to "confuse the map for the territory." I pointed out that there were different ways of visualizing the future, such as symbolic and metaphorical images, that may not as easily lead to disappointment because the images had more flexibility built into them and were less likely to be confused for "reality."

I asked if she still had any resistance to putting her eyes up and to the right and imagining how she would like things to be. She responded that she didn't think it was such a big issue any longer, so I said, "Well, let's try it out a few times and see." I had her look up and picture a more positive future once, twice, three times, four times...And after about the fifth time, there was a markedly visible change in her physiology. Her resistance had vanished and in its place was a sense of both confidence and excitement.

As a closure to the session, I asked her to look into her future and create a new image of herself that in some way synthesized the two symbolic pictures she had made of her conflicting parts into a unified image of herself. I invited her to visualize the two parts of herself as no longer separated but integrated together into one whole, "successful human being" combining the positive purposes and capabilities of both parts that had previously been in conflict. She saw a mother eagle soaring through the air to a nest, high up in the top of a tree where it was safe and there was a very wide view of the surrounding environment. The sharp eyed eagle could see very far in its ability to assess the present conditions around it, so that it could prepare for the future in the most effective way.

As you might imagine, this woman started really changing after that. All of a sudden a lot of positive shifts began to occur in her life. It was just a little thing we had done in a way...a little breakthrough. But she had shifted a deep presupposition about her relationship to past and future through this process. She realized she could make something familiar. And when that something is the ability to visualize your future, it can turn you into a veritable Einstein.

To me, this is a good example of applying the same strategy Einstein used to arrive at his theory of relativity to help solve a psychological or "human" problem. The purpose of the strategy is finding the presupposition that makes two frames of reference incompatible and then jump to another level of thinking in order to solve the problem.

Einstein's strategy for resolving conflict is very similar to a basic change process in NLP known as "reframing." The basic method of reframing involves looking beyond a particular problematic behavior to the 'positive intention' that is behind it. A typical approach to conflict resolution in NLP is to first "chunk up" one level above the conflict to find consensus with respect to "higher level" values. A second step involves "chunking down" one level below the level at which the conflict is taking place. At this "lower level" it is possible to find "complementary" resources related to the parts of the system which are seemingly in conflict.

**Consensus in Relation to
Intention on Higher Level**

↑

Level of Conflict

↓

**Complementary Resources
on Lower Level**

**Solving a Problem Through a Different Level of
Thinking Than is Creating the Problem**

In the example with the depressed woman, she had a conflict on the level of her *beliefs and values* related to the past and future. She experienced a polarization between the part of herself that wanted to protect her and the part of herself that believed she needed to grow. Trying to solve the problem at the same level of thinking that was creating it led her into a double bind.

The solution came through "chunking up" to the level of *identity* and finding the common purpose of the positive intentions behind the conflicting parts of herself. Once the level at which there was 'consensus' between the parts was identified we "chunked down" to the level of *capability*. At this level we were able to identify 'complementary' resources associated with each of the conflicting parts that could be used in service of the positive intention of the other parts.

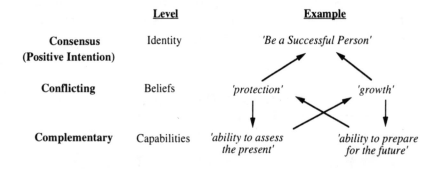

**"Chunking Up" and "Chunking Down" To Find
A Solution to Conflicting Beliefs and Values**

In the process of arriving at the theory of relativity, one of the presuppositions Einstein challenged was that of "simultaneity" - that is, that the observers in each frame of reference were actually seeing the same event at the same time. This is also a common unconscious presupposition influencing personal problems as well. Different frames of reference, or beliefs, are developed at different times in one's life. As in the example of the depressed woman, many beliefs that make up a person's model of the world are in fact established in childhood. These beliefs are often limited in their scope and perspective, but seem more 'real' because they are more familiar and have more personal experiences and memories to back them up than those established later in life. Rather than perceive all beliefs as being "simultaneous" it is often helpful to find the time of origin of a particular belief or frame of reference so that it may be placed and evaluated with respect to its appropriate time frame (Freud would no doubt also agree with this). It is then possible to move to another level of perceiving the conflict.

The notion of different levels of thinking and being is a very important one in understanding and applying Einstein's strategy. For instance, geniuses are typically said to think on a "higher level" than other people.   Likewise, personal experience and changes also occur on different 'levels'. In our brain structure, language, and perceptual systems there are, in fact, naturally occurring levels of classification.   Our mental strategies are organized into levels of thinking as well. The effect of each level is to register and respond to relationships between events on the level below it. Changing something on an upper level would necessarily influence relationships on the lower levels; changing something on a lower level could but would not necessarily effect the upper levels. In my work with NLP, I organize these levels into the categories listed below:

Spiritual - *Sense of Being a Part of a Larger System*

a. Who I Am - *Sense of Personal Identity*

b. My Belief System and Values - *Presuppositions about reality*

c. My Capabilities - *Thinking Strategies and Mental Maps*

d. What I Do or have Done - *Specific Behaviors and Actions*

e. My Environment - *External Constraints*

* *Environmental factors* determine the external constraints a person has to react to. Answer to the questions **where?** and **when?**

* *Behavior* is made up of the specific actions taken within the environment. Answer to the question **what?**

* *Capabilities* guide and give direction to behavioral actions through a mental map, path or strategy. Answer to the question **how?**

* *Beliefs* and *values* provide the reinforcement (motivation and permission) that supports, or denies, capabilities. Answer to the question **why?**

* *Identity* factors determine overall vision or purpose (mission) and shape beliefs and values. Answer to the question **who?**

* The *spiritual* has to do with our experience of being a part of a much vaster system than our own identity ("mission" and "trans-mission").

At the lowest levels we perform **specific behaviors** within a specific set of **external constraints**. These behaviors, however, are like knee jerk reactions, habits or rituals. At the level of **capability** we are able to select, alter and adapt a class of behaviors to more general contexts. At the level of **beliefs** we may encourage, inhibit or generalize a whole class of behavior. **Identity**, of course, consolidates whole systems of beliefs. On the relational and **'spiritual'** levels above identity, we perceive ourselves to be part of larger and larger systems around us: family, professional community, global community, even our place in the universe. This level relates to our sense of overall 'mission' and purpose.

While each level becomes more abstracted from the specifics of behavior and sensory experience, it actually has more and more widespread effect on our behavior and experience.

Each of the levels involves a different kind of organization
and evaluation that will select, access and utilize the information on the level below it.   In this way they form a
relational network as shown in the following diagram.

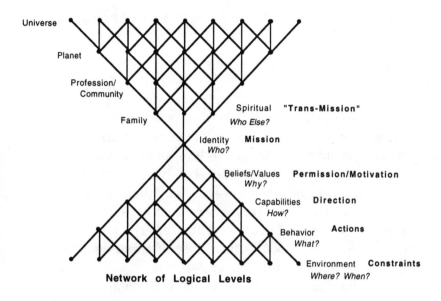

Relationship of Different Levels of Experience

Anthropologist Gregory Bateson pointed out that in many
areas of behavior and communication people mixed or confused such *"logical levels"*, which could create problems.
There is a big difference, for instance, between having a
drink (specific behavior) and being **an** 'alcoholic' (identity), or
between having a tumor and being **a** 'cancer victim'. As an
example of how the different levels may become confused,
consider a student who does not do well on a particular test
in school.   He or she can respond to it on a number of
different levels:

a. Identity: *"I am a stupid/learning disabled person."*

b. Belief/Values: *"Learning is difficult and boring."*

c. Capability: *"I am not very good at taking examinations."*

d. Behavior: *"I did not do well on this particular exam."*

e. Environment: *"Something in the room distracted me."*

One implication of this is that conflicts can occur on several different levels. In the example of the depressed woman, the conflict was on the level of beliefs and values - which is the most common level at which conflicts occur. There may be conflicts, however, on other levels. For instance, a person may experience conflict between their capabilities to be "logical" versus "intuitive." The person may be stuck or confused about which type of thinking process to apply to a particular problem or decision.

Resolving this level of conflict may be done in much the same way as resolving conflicts of beliefs and values - through (a) "chunking up" a level to find the positive intentions or purposes of the two different ways of thinking, and then (b) chunking down to find how the subprocesses or results of the two different capabilities can actually complement and support each other.

In the case of a conflict between "logical" and "intuitive" thinking, The common purpose at the level of intention may be at the values level, such as "finding the most effective solution." The complementary processes associated with the different capabilities may be at the level of behavioral results. Logical thinking, for example, produces the result of "sorting something according to linear order and sequence." This order and sequence may actually serve to stimulate new intuitions. Intuitive thinking, on the other hand, produces the behavioral result of "sorting something according to meaning and nonlinear relationships." These meanings and relationships may then be ordered and sequenced according to logical thinking. This seems to me to be an integration that Einstein was able to achieve to a high degree.

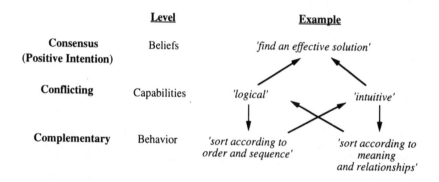

Resolving a Conflict at the Level of Capability by "Chunking Up" and "Chunking Down" to Other Levels

Perhaps the most challenging conflicts are those which occur at the level of identity. Many of us experience the tension between being a "parent" versus a "career person" or between being a "spouse" versus an "individual," etc. It seems that through his theory of relativity, and the strategy that led him to this theory, Einstein was able to resolve the conflicts that faced him in his dual identity as "scientist" and "philosopher."

Resolving conflicts related to identity involve "chunking up" to a level beyond one's own identity. Accomplishing this requires that we are able to widen our maps of the world to be able to perceive ourselves as part of the larger systems around us in order to get a sense of overall 'mission' and purpose.

Einstein concluded that his common mission as both "scientist" and "philosopher" was the task to "widen our circle of compassion, to embrace all living creatures and the whole of nature in its beauty." The beliefs, values and capabilities of a "scientist" are oriented around deepening our knowledge of "what is." The beliefs, values and capabilities of a "philosopher" are dedicated to exploring what "should be" or "could be." Einstein was clearly able to use these as complementary resources in the service of his mission.

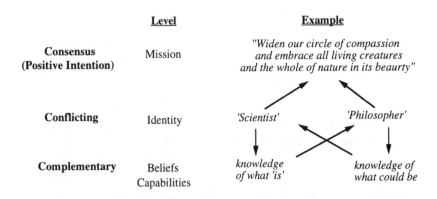

Integrating Potentially Conflicting Identities
In the Service of a Common Spiritual Mission

One's full identity is the entire ocean, not simply the different fish that swim in it. One's true identity is not any particular image or system of measurement, but rather the light that makes both the image and the measurement possible.

Perhaps it is no accident that so many great people throughout history have equated identity and spirit with light. When one aligns or identifies oneself with either the 'flesh' or the 'spirit', body or mind, the ego or the id, the left brain or the right brain, logic or imagination, stability or change, then one has created an imbalance and a potential conflict. When one identifies oneself with something more like the light, then one can see that it is the relationship between these elements that is important. Evolution and adaptation, for instance, are a function of a process of change on an individual level and a process of stabilization on a larger environmental level. Personal evolution requires the same balance of forces at different logical levels.

Clearly, sorting experiences into their appropriate levels can help resolve a lot of confusion and trouble. It seems to me that what Einstein accomplished with the theory of relativity was the resorting of the conflicting frames of reference in physics from the level of **identity** to the level of **belief** so that a deeper and broader truth at the identity level could be discovered. He then related this change to larger and larger systems. Indeed, Einstein's ability to recognize the different logical levels and sort experiences into their appropriate levels in order to resolve problems was not only an ability that changed him, it changed the world.

Footnotes to Chapter 7

1. J. Schwartz & M. McGuinness, *Einstein For Beginners*,
Pantheon Books, New York, New York, 1983, p. 3.

Chapter 8

Applications of Einstein's Strategy

The objective of the modeling process is not to end up with the one 'right' or 'true' description of a particular person's thinking process, but rather to make an instrumental map that allows us to apply the strategies that we have modeled in some useful way. An 'instrumental map' is one that allows us to act more effectively - the 'accuracy' or 'reality' of the map is less important than its 'elegance' and 'usefulness'. A metaphorical map, such as Einstein's 'thought experiments', may have as much instrumental value as a 'realistic' map. For instance, the symbolic images of the depressed woman, described in the previous chapter, carried much more important information about her identity and beliefs than accurate photographic representations would have.

The instrumental application of the micro, macro and meta strategies that we have modeled from a particular individual involves putting them into structures that allow us to use them for some practical purpose. One way to think about practically applying the information modeled from an individual's mental strategies is that it may be implemented with respect to different parts of the T.O.T.E. That is, we may identify and apply a person's *goals* only; using other operations to achieve those goals and other evidence procedures to assess progress towards the goals. Or, we may model the *operations* of an individual and apply those operations to achieve different goals than those for which they were originally intended. We may also choose to identify and use only the *evidences* or *evidence procedures* used by the model, applying them to different goals and with different operations than those for which they were originally developed.

Thus, we may use all or only parts of the information we have modeled from a particular genius. In Einstein's case, for example, we can apply the strategies we have modeled by:

a) applying them to areas other than physics,

b) combining elements of his strategies with other methods and approaches in order to enhance and enrich them, or

c) using them as the inspiration for building a completely new approach to thinking about something.

For instance, let's say we take Einstein's use of "thought experiments" and his application of analogies to "pace and lead" from two-dimensional thinking to three dimensional thinking and finally to four dimensional spherical space. One question would be, "How could we apply these 'operations' to help in finding solutions to problems and goals other than the ones Einstein originally used them for?" Another question might be, "What other operations might be suggested by these strategies?" A third question might be, "What other tools or operations could be developed to assist people in using and applying these strategies more effectively?"

Seeing New Levels and Dimensions

As an example of how we might approach answering some of the questions just posed, consider the following process inspired by Einstein's strategies. A good metaphor and tool for the process viewing something from a 'third position' in order to get a 'double description' and literally seeing other "dimensions" and "levels" is provided by the "STARE-E-O's" developed by N.E. Thing Enterprises.[1] "STARE-E-O's" are three dimensional 'pictures' created by applying an image rendering system known as the "Salitsky Dot" to embed a three dimensional image in a two dimensional surface.

I made the following STARE-E-O using the Depthmaker computer software by Daniel Dyckman.[2]

When you first look at the picture, it appears to be a chaotic, undecipherable mass of dots. Yet if you are able to focus your eyes in the proper way, you will see that there is actually a very specific and clear 'image' there - in another dimension. The particular 'image' is of the Chinese "yin and yang" symbol.

The basic steps for seeing the image amidst the seeming chaos are:

1. Look at the picture and relax.

2. Focus your eyes as if you are looking at a faraway object behind the picture (this is known as "diverging"). A three dimensional image should begin to materialize.

3. If not, hold the picture against your nose and very slowly pull it away from your face.

Not everyone can see these images right away, so don't worry if you are having a difficult time at first. Sometimes people struggle and struggle to see them and when they finally give up the image suddenly jumps out at them. What is important to realize is that if you look *at* the picture, you will never see the image. You must look "through" the picture. I suggest that you view the image as if you were Einstein gazing deeply into space, considering the mysteries of the cosmos.

In the model of NLP, the physiology that we assume while we are thinking of something has a tremendous influence. Subtle cues such as our breathing rate, posture and eye position stimulate and direct our thinking process. The type of 'soft focus' required to view a STARE-E-O is also an important "accessing cue." To me, this experience is a deep metaphor and a tool for developing Einstein's way of looking at the world and the universe.

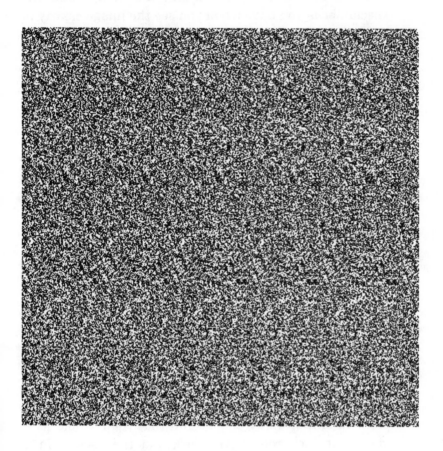

'STARE-E-O' of Six Spheres

When you have had some experience viewing the images, try the following "thought experiment."

1. Think of a problem you are struggling with. Especially one that involves relationships with others.

2. Look at the STARE-E-O above or on the earlier page. Notice both the 'actively open' focus you enter into as

you are first attempting to find the image, and the special focus you have when you see the image clearly in three dimensions.

3. As you are bringing the other dimension and level of the image into focus, simply think about the problem you have been struggling with.

   Again, as you maintain that focus, imagine you are in the shoes of Albert Einstein looking for the hidden dimensions in the universe, considering the mysteries of space and time. Pretend you could be in the mind of Einstein and tap into his genius and wisdom. Like Einstein you can be riding on the end of a light beam or moving in and out of the flat worlds of two-dimensional beings into the four dimensional space-time continuum. You can be in an elevator pulled through space by a fantastic being or in a tram that travels faster than the speed of light back in time. Realize that you can challenge basic assumptions, just as Einstein did, and expand the limits of your model of the world to "free yourself" from the "prison" of your own thinking.

4. Notice how your perception and relationship to that problem shifts. Many people find that their whole feeling about the problem changes, and they see it in a completely different 'perspective'.

NOTE: Another tool I have developed for harnessing and applying the influence of one's internal state is the *NeuroLink*, a type of biofeedback device which simultaneously monitors and records activity in heart rate, body temperature and the brain hemispheres via patterns of electrical activity on the left and right sides of the body. The NeuroLink comes with software which combines these key measurements of nervous system activity with artificial intelligence and NLP methods and principles to help people achieve optimal states of health, learning and personal performance. The device and software are available through NeuroLink International of Scotts Valley, California.

Using Symbolic Metaphors to Find and Challenge Basic Assumptions

Another approach to applying what we have modeled from Einstein is to select certain elements of his strategy, and then modify and synthesize them into a more generalized problem solving structure. The following process is a formulation of how one might use key elements of Einstein's strategy as a general problem solving format.

1. Make a concise description or statement defining the problem you are confronting. It helps to write it down and underline any key words that might seem especially ambiguous or problematic.

2. Draw a picture (an "imaginary construction") representing a problem you are currently trying to solve. The picture should be a sketch, a metaphor, or symbolic representation. It is important to make sure that you form your image such that you can enter into each frame of reference implied by your visualization and view the problem from each different point of view.

3. Explore the beliefs, values and assumptions presupposed by your representation of the problem space. For each key element (or visualizing symbol) in the picture, ask yourself "What are the assumptions presupposed by that representation?"

4. Find a frame of reference outside of the problem space of any conflicting frames of reference (meta position). That is, find a new way of viewing or thinking about the problem that is different from the way of thinking that is creating the problem. This may be done by:

   a. Changing the time frame from which you are operating - changing from short term to long term, from present to past, or from short term future to long term future, etc.

   b. Finding a completely new point of view from which to consider the problem. (You might even wonder, how would Albert Einstein view this problem?)

   c. Shifting the level from which you are considering the problem - i.e., if you've been thinking about it as a problem relating to beliefs and values (a 'why' issue), try considering it purely from the environmental or behavioral level; if you've been thinking of it as a behavioral difficulty, consider it from the level of identity or mission, etc.

This should allow you to begin to move to a different level of thinking about the problem.

5. Widen your map and explore possible additional 'solution space' and resources by considering in what ways you could change or enrich your perception of the problem by:

   a. Remaking your picture or visual construction of the problem.

   b. Reconsidering the beliefs, values and assumptions you are presupposing with respect to the problem.

6. Explore how making these changes or additions to your mental map, assumptions and beliefs would alter or enrich your perception of or approach to the problem. Identify and write down, or note any new possible solutions that occur to you.

As a simple illustration of the purpose and value of this strategy, consider for a moment the following problem:

A police officer on traffic duty saw a bus driver going the wrong way down a one way street, yet the police officer did not issue the bus driver a ticket. Why?

Before going on, write down your answer and how you arrived at it. Pay attention to what kinds of mental maps you made of the situation to arrive at your answer.

Because the problem has been defined verbally, we must make many unconscious assumptions about the situation. In this case, the key to the seeming anomaly revolves around presuppositions related to the 'words' and 'word-combinations' "bus driver" and "going." Most people assume that the "bus driver" is inside of a bus and that "going" means 'driving the bus.' If we realize that the bus driver could be walking down the street, the seeming anomaly is resolved.

Einstein's approach to this problem would have no doubt been to find the words that are most visually ambiguous, such as "going," and then try to form a symbolic but clear cognitive map of the interaction defined by the problem, forming an imaginary visual construction and putting himself in the perceptual positions of both the bus driver and the police officer. To construct a clear picture of the problem that is being described (such as a symbolic drawing) you would have to at some point consciously put the bus driver into a bus. This would create the opportunity to discover the assumption rather than simply considering the problem verbally.

As a way to try out this strategy, let us return to the problem of the factory posed at the beginning of the chapter on Einstein's basic strategy and use the steps I have just described to rethink it. Let's see how much your thinking has been influenced by the intervening chapters on Einstein's thinking processes.

You are the person in charge of factory "B". The chief of your maintenance Department manages 6 eight man teams, working under 6 foremen. You are worried because these teams don't work efficiently. As a matter of fact, the workers in the teams tend to do just what strictly concerns their specific tasks. As a result, work and programs of this Department are slowed down. Only in cases of emergency is this routine overcome. You also know, on the other hand, that the capabilities and competence of the workers are higher and allow for more effective utilization.

How would you approach solving this problem?

Draw a picture representing your understanding of the problem space described in the scenario on a separate piece of paper and write a short description of your approach to reaching a solution. The picture may be a sketch, a metaphor, or symbolic representation.

Now, go back over the scenario, your picture and your approach to the problem and find out what you have assumed or presupposed by your representation of the problem space. Compare your current ideas of how to approach the situation with the ideas you outlined when you considered this problem earlier in this book. As you contrast your first approach to the one you just defined, consider the following questions:

What did you assume about the where, when, what, how, why and who of the problem situation?

Did you assume it was a "how to" problem or a "want to" problem"?

Did you assume it was a problem of motivation? Of organization? Of communication? Of leadership?

From whose perspective did you form your imaginary construction? The person in charge of the factory? The chief of maintenance? The foremen? The workers?

What did you assume about the perspective and values of the person in charge of the factory? The chief of maintenance? The foremen? The workers?

What did you assume was the cause of the problem? The person in charge of the factory? The chief of maintenance? The foremen? The workers? Factors coming from parts of the organization other than the ones described in the problem statement?

What kind of visualization of the system and the problem did you make?

Did you mentally simulate any scenarios or interactions?

There is obviously no right answer to this problem, and finding a specific solution is not the point to this particular "thought experiment." Its purpose is to help you become more aware of your own thinking process so you can identify and challenge your own mental maps and assumptions - as Einstein did when he delved into his own psychological presuppositions about the conception of space and time.

This strategy, however, can certainly be applied to reach solutions to real problems. For example, I once consulted with a man who was in a situation somewhat similar to the problem in the factory. He was a project leader in charge of a group of engineers working to develop products in a technology company. His problem, as he described it, was that at the beginning of a project he would call a meeting of the team members in which he would communicate very clearly and precisely to his project team the type of product they were to make; how it was to look and how it needed to operate. He would then clearly specify the roles, and responsibilities of each team member. Next, he checked with all the group members to make sure that their understanding of his instructions was clear. When he was satisfied that they understood, he would send them out to work on the project. Invariably, as time went on, the team members and thus the project would become progressively more inefficient, slowing everything down and producing errors that the team leader would have to correct.

Employing Einstein's strategy, I asked him to create a symbolic metaphor of the problem. The image he made depicted himself as a source of light, like a lighthouse. He imagined a bright red light emanating from his head to his team members, whom he imagined as being like ships floating in the ocean. While the ships were nearby, his light could guide them to see the way to their destination and avoid the rocks near the shoreline. But as the ship got farther away, the ships lost sight of the guiding light and began to flounder at sea.

We then began to seek out the assumptions that were presupposed by his problem description and his symbolic construction. One important assumption was that light was sufficient for navigation. He realized that the purpose of a lighthouse was only to provide a reference point and help people avoid shipwrecks while they were in the locality. Another assumption was that the ships did not have their own sources of light and that they were always sailing in the dark.

I asked him to take the perceptual position of the team members and imagine how they would perceive his communications and his role as a leader. His sense was that, while they respected and understood him, his clarity about the design and responsibilities related to the project made it obvious that it was his project and not theirs; so they lacked the feeling of enthusiasm that comes with ownership - they did not identify with the project. Furthermore, while they understood his instructions to them clearly as individuals, they did not have a map of the whole project. While they understood on an information level, they did not really know how their individual actions coordinated with the actions of the other team members in the ongoing process.

As a result of this, I invited him to change some of his assumptions and alter his imaginary construction to create a different approach. He visualized himself again as a type of light house. But instead of sending out a bright red light for short periods of time, he saw himself emanating a soft constant pink light. After a period of time, sparks of pink and reddish lights began to flicker into small flames on board some of the ships. If he kept the pink light shining long enough, all of the ships would have their own flames burning. By his maintaining the pink light the flames on board the ships would begin to burn larger and brighter, casting light and providing guidance for one another as well.

He then implemented this symbolic plan by using many of the elements of Einstein's strategy. Rather than describe the project clearly and precisely, he would start by giving only a general overview or outline of the project. He would then have the team members individually draw their own pictures in the form of imaginary constructs of symbolic metaphors of what they thought he meant. He would then have everyone compare and explain their pictures and explore the assumptions they each had about the project and their various roles and responsibilities. Since the project leader had already thought the project through thoroughly and had a clear idea of the issues involved in the project, he could be more of a guide or coach to help all of the different members discover key assumptions or beliefs. Not only did this solve many of the motivational and conceptual problems that had been making the team inefficient; the team members themselves adopted it as a general problem solving process amongst themselves.

As this example implies, Einstein's strategy can also be adapted to team learning and problem solving contexts. The following steps summarize how the process could be carried out with a group or team.

1. Person A describes a problem or goal to the other group members.

2. Each person in the group (including person A) individually draws a picture representing his or her own understanding of the problem space. The picture may be a sketch, a metaphor, or a symbolic representation.

3. All group members share, compare and explain their pictures. Explore the beliefs, values and assumptions presupposed by each person about their representation of the problem space.
For each key element (visualizing symbol) in the picture, ask "What are the assumptions behind your choice of that representation?"

4. As a group, discuss and identify the assumptions, beliefs or values that could be added or changed in the cluster of beliefs and values that currently underlie the explorer's approach to the problem. Explore how making these changes or additions to the explorer's assumptions and beliefs would alter or enrich his or her perception of the problem.

5. Each group member, including the explorer who is to go last, makes a representation of the 'solution space' he or she thinks would be most valuable to the explorer.

To make their individual representations, group members may either:

a) make a new map.

b) add directly to their previous map of the problem space.

c) add directly to the explorer's map of the problem space.

d) present a metaphor or analogy.

6. Explore how making these changes or additions to your assumptions and beliefs would alter or enrich person A's perception of the problem.

As an example of the application of how this process can be applied, I was recently involved in an intervention with a large European transportation company that was moving from being a state run organization to becoming privatized. The transition was causing a lot of turmoil within various divisions of the organization.

As a component of my part of the intervention, I assembled a group of individuals from various functions within the organization and had the members of the group each create their own symbolic image of the problem situation in their company.

One person described their situation as being like a group of sailors on a sailing ship that each had many tasks to do on board the ship. Under normal circumstances the sailors could both do their jobs and communicate with one another. But in a stormy sea, the sailors had to focus so much on their own tasks that they did not have the opportunity to interact with one another, making it more difficult to coordinate their activities.

Another individual viewed the situation as being like an astronaut whose capsule had landed on a planet that had no natural resources to sustain the astronaut. The astronaut was trying to salvage as many supplies and pieces of equipment as he could in order to survive on the planet.

One individual saw the situation as if the company were a dysfunctional family. Another perceived it as also being like a family, but a normal one. She saw their situation as being similar to that of an adolescent preparing to leave home and live on his or her own for the first time.

By comparing their different symbolic images, the group members were able to hear and understand their different perspectives without having to feel like they needed to defend their map of the situation. Rather than arguing about whose perception was the 'right map', they were more easily able to perceive and explore the assumptions presupposed by the various symbolic images, and to discover hidden strengths as well.

For instance, both the metaphor of the ship and the astronaut's capsule assumed a challenging environment, but one presupposed the problem as being a communication issue between a group of crew members, whereas the astronaut was all alone. And it was significant that the problem on board the ship was one of communication between the crew as opposed to poor leadership on the part of the captain.

By going back and forth between the different metaphors, the group began to become aware of what was the same between the various perspectives and which assumptions could be challenged and changed. As a result of this process, the group was able to communicate about their differences in perception with less tension, anxiety and defensiveness. They also had several new perspectives and metaphors from which to view their situation. This allowed them to explore innovative solutions because they were approaching the problem with a "different type of thinking" than they had done previously.

A Format for Resolving Conflicts Based on Einstein's Strategy

In the previous chapter, I discussed some of the psychological implications of Einstein's theory of relativity and gave an example of how the strategy Einstein used while developing the theory could be used to help resolve psychological conflicts.* Below are a set of steps, based on Einstein's thinking strategy, that can be applied to help people resolve conflicts of beliefs or identity. These steps both review and apply the most important psychological aspects of Einstein's strategy for the integration of opposing frames of reference.

1. Identify the antagonistic frames of reference associated with the change; i.e., the 'first' and 'second' positions. The conflict may involve yourself and another person, two others in conflict or two parts of yourself in conflict; e.g. the woman's conflict between wanting to change and fear of change.

2. Establish a 'third position' or 'meta position' that is outside of either of the two positions in conflict. As much as possible identify the underlying assumptions associated with the conflict; e.g. the universe is "unfriendly."

3. Form symbolic or metaphoric images representing each of the conflicting positions; e.g. the "butterfly" and the "mother dinosaur."

---

* NLP has a number of techniques and formats for resolving conflicts and changing limiting beliefs. For some examples, see *NLP Vol. I* (1980), *Beliefs: Pathways to Health and Well Being* (1990) and *Changing Beliefs with NLP* (1990).

4. Put yourself into each perceptual position as completely as possible and identify the positive intention or purpose of each position. e.g. the positive intent of the "butterfly" was "growth," the positive intent of the "dinosaur" was "survival" and "protection."

5. Identify the common purpose of both positive intentions at the higher level; e.g. "being a successful human being."

6. Identify the 'complementary' capabilities of each position; that is the capabilities that one position has that can actually help the other accomplish its own positive intention more effectively. e.g. The "butterfly's" ability to "prepare for the future" and the dinosaur's ability to "assess the present."

7. Return to a meta position and form a new symbolic image of the two positions working in unity and harmony; e.g. the "mother eagle in her nest."

In the previous chapter, I gave an example of applying this strategy to a woman who had a serious personal problem. The following example illustrates how the same strategy could be applied to help solve a relational problem in a business context.

I once consulted with a young man who was in a crisis because of a promotion. Before this promotion he had always gotten along very well with all of his co-workers. He was a highly relational person. He really stood up for his colleagues and helped them with their work. He covered for them if they weren't able to complete a job or could have gotten into trouble. So the company said, "This guy is good! We will make him their manager."

So there he was, suddenly their manager. And all his co-workers said, "Great, we can get away with whatever we want now. He will cover for us just like he always did. He is one of us!"

This is where his crisis started. He said, "Wait a minute! I don't have the same relationship with you anymore. I have a responsibility for a larger system of things now. The values I have to uphold in the larger system with my new role and the evaluation of my behavior by my own managers are completely different now. From this new frame of reference, I can't ecologically do those kinds of things anymore from my new position in the system."

Then all the things which got him promoted started working against him. His co-workers said, "Traitor, jerk,..." His own manager said, "Hey, what's going on. You're supposed to be getting along with these guys. Your performance is falling off. If you can't keep these guys under control we're going to have to let you go." He really felt like he was in a double bind. From one frame of reference he felt responsible for his co-workers, from another frame of reference he had responsibilities to his own manager and to his company.

As a part of our work, I asked him to create a symbolic image of the conflict situation. He pictured himself as a crew member on an old time sailing ship. His boss was a naval officer (a bit like Captain Bligh of the Bounty) and his co-workers were like a mutinous crew. Because he had shown qualities of positive leadership, the captain had taken him away from the rest of his duties as a crew member to help maintain order. But the captain had given him a whip to use, which he felt uncomfortable with and which inspired fear and hatred in the crew members.

We then established a frame of reference outside of that whole problem space - a meta position where he could look at all the members of the system, including himself. The next step was to identify assumptions that were being presupposed in the conflict and were being reflected in his symbolic construction.

He realized that the feelings of his co-workers came from the presupposition that you *needed* protection from the company - that the company was foreign and hostile to them.

The presupposition behind the response of his own manager was that the workers needed external controls to get them to work. The common assumption was that they were not part of the same system or team. Neither the presuppositions of his former co-workers or his own boss were based on facts or personal contact between workers and company management. Instead they were both presuppositions about how companies functioned that had been around historically and had gone unquestioned.

The workers felt that they needed to "get away with" something because the rules that set their work patterns were out of their hands and were unresponsive to the needs they had within the reality of their jobs. The company's upper management felt the workers needed to be controlled because they were constantly breaking the rules.

I asked the manager to put himself into the perspectives of the conflicting positions and find the positive intention of each one. He concluded that the positive intention of the "crew" of co-workers was to be able to do their job with a sense of camaraderie with their fellow workers and with the minimum amount of external interference. The positive intention of the boss or "captain" was to run an orderly ship that was able to operate smoothly enough to fulfill its mission.

I also had him consider the problem from the point of view of his own broader mission and identity. He determined that his own positive intention was to be a key player on a effective team.

We then discussed that it was important to acknowledge the beliefs and values of all the different points of view, but in the end no one frame of reference was the ultimate reality.

We began looking for what was common to all the perspectives and intentions. What seemed to be the constant in all of the perspectives was the desire for consideration and acknowledgment as being an important member of the system or team, and participation as a "team member."

As a result, the young manager realized that if the workers felt like they had an opportunity to offer input regarding the organizational rules that affected their working environment, they would not need to get away with anything because they would be participating in their own management.   If they felt like they were a 'part of' the company they would be more motivated to work because it was in their own best interest.

Likewise if the upper management could see that the workers were taking responsibility for their own scheduling and productivity, they would not feel the need to exert controls over them. The company could then become more responsive to the needs of the workers out of its own best interest.

At this point, as with Einstein, his ability to experience things from multiple frames of reference became an advantage for the young manager instead of creating a double bind. He found that he could translate between the frames of reference for both the workers and the upper management.

When I asked him to reform his image of the situation, he laughed confidently and said that his "bull whip" had turned into a "bull horn."

A Strategy for 'Mediation' Based on Einstein's Thinking Process

The following process is a short summary of another variation on Einstein's basic strategy that can be used to help 'mediate' between individuals (or parts of oneself) that are in conflict.

To begin, identify a 1 to 1 situation involving someone you find to be resistant (or two others in conflict or two parts of yourself in conflict). Lay out three physical locations for 1st, 2nd and 3rd position.

('Mediator Position')
Third Position

First Position   Second Position

Spatial Locations for Different Perceptual Positions

1. Enter into the 1st position location and imagine that the person (or part) is presently in front of you and interacting with you. Imagine the range of possible behaviors that could create problems.

2. Take a point of view to the interaction as if you were seeing it from the perspective of someone who has the best interest of the system in mind ('Mediator Position').

Observe the 1st position behavior in relation to the other person.

3. Now imagine you were "in the shoes" (2nd position) of the other person (or part). How do you experience the 1st position behavior from the perspective of the other?

   a. Are there any other influences on this person/part of yourself from outside of the physical sphere of the interaction that you notice and need to add to the map?

   b. If you were in the world view of the other person/part, what would be the positive intention behind your behavior in this interaction?

4. Go back to the mediator perspective and create a symbolic map of the two conflicting positions and identify the underlying assumptions at the base of the conflict.

5. Then determine:

   a. The positive intent of each of the two positions in conflict.

   b. A common criterion on a higher level encompassing the positive intentions of both of the positions in conflict.

   c. What complementary capabilities/resources the two positions have that could actually be used to support one another.

   (See examples in the previous chapter.)

6. Imagine how you might make the appropriate alterations to messages, mental maps or interactions in order to clarify, align or balance the interaction within the context of the common criterion. Consider how you can incorporate all of the relevant perspectives and intentions to reach a common goal or purpose.

7. Remake your symbolic map, incorporating the changes and solutions you have discovered.

Footnotes to Chapter 8

1. N.E. Thing Enterprises, One Kendall Square, Building 200, Cambridge, MA, 02139.

2. *Depthmaker*, Daniel Dyckman, 300 First Avenue #4-B, New York, New York, 1991.

Chapter 9

Summary of Einstein's Thinking Process

Synthesizing all of the information we have uncovered about Einstein's mental strategies in the previous chapters, we can summarize the basic elements of his thinking process in the following steps.

1. Begin with sensory experience.

The purpose of creating a model is to organize and interact with the sensory world around us. It *"owes its meaning and its justification exclusively to the totality of the sense impressions which we associate with it."* In order to be useful, all models must be grounded in sensory experience.

2. Identify the fundamental elements in the system to be modeled (i.e., the 'first' and 'second' positions).

These fundamental elements are derived initially by finding *"certain repeatedly occurring complexes of sense impressions"* (i.e., patterns) from the associated sequences of "memory pictures" we have pulled "out of the multitude of our sense experiences." These patterns and concepts are initially drawn directly from our sensory experiences but will begin to go beyond what we have perceived or experienced as we get closer to the 'generating rules' of the system we are trying to model. In other words, we begin to find more fundamental patterns between the surface level patterns, and then patterns of patterns of patterns, etc.

3. Use constructed visual "images" to represent these basic elements.

Because the more fundamental patterns begin to deviate increasingly from what can actually be sensed, we must use imaginary constructs to represent these elements. While the purpose of these imaginary constructs is to generalize and simplify the complex   representations from our incoming sensory "labyrinth" in order to arrive at *"a minimum of primary concepts and relations,"* we must be careful about moving too far too quickly from sensory experience. Mathematical and verbal constructs for instance can be, on the one hand too tied to the specific processes of measuring and statistics to allow for creativity, and on the other hand, too distant from sensory experience to be intuitively connected to what one is trying to model.

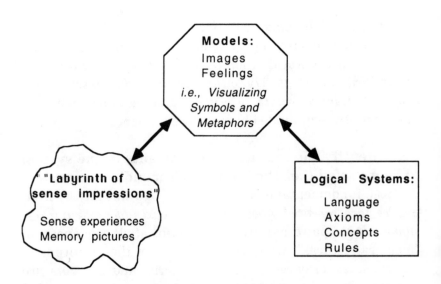

Visualizing Symbols Integrate Sensory Experience and Logical Systems

In Einstein's case, it seems that imagination primarily functioned through visual images of somewhat simple visual elements ("*visualizing symbols*") like geometric shapes and atoms; or visual metaphors like the blind beetle or riding on the end of a light beam.   The purpose of this type of imagination was to extend and simplify our concepts of the world in order to elucidate the "*interactions of elementary bodies*" in "*a totality of systems.*"   By beginning with sensory experience and finding the more general patterns level-by-level, you also leave a sort of 'trail of derivations' by which you can always trace your path back to sensory experience. Furthermore, by systematically going through the levels, each level will incorporate the information about the level below it, and there will be less chance that an important element of the system will be accidently omitted.

For Einstein this process resulted in the discovery of two seemingly different perceptual positions or systems that interacted together in a manner that was unclear or para-doxical - for example, moving versus stationary observer; matter versus energy; particles of light versus light waves; three dimensional versus four dimensional systems; experi-ence versus logic.

4. Begin to freely engage in "combinatory play" with the elements, switching back and forth between the different frames of reference.

Fully explore what each frame of reference is like by placing yourself into it so that you can fully see and feel what it is like to operate from that perceptual space. Then, once each system (perceptual position) has been fully explored individually and in one's own imagination, go back and forth between both systems and try to determine intuitively (most likely through a feeling) which aspects of the transformation between the two stay constant.

5. Move to a broader "visual survey" that encompasses the other systems or perceptual positions (third position).

Once the "associative play is sufficiently established and can be reproduced at will," the movement between the two basic positions will eventually lead to a 'third position' - a larger frame of reference in which the relationship between the two systems in question is clear.

6. Make an explicit description of the "generating rules" that have been seen or felt from the 'third position'.

At this stage we may now coordinate and connect the relationship that is seen and felt from the broader survey of 'third position' with verbal and/or mathematical concepts and propositions so that it may be further simplified and communicated to others. This process, naturally, requires that one be familiar with the appropriate verbal or mathematical structures (or to make up such a system, as Newton did when he invented differential calculus to describe his discoveries with gravity).

Had Einstein not been able to represent the fruits of his imagination mathematically his discoveries may have gone completely unnoticed by the scientific community.

Of course, by the same token, there have been many, many individuals that have been trained in the explicit mathematical model that Einstein used whom, because they were missing the first part of the strategy, did not produce discoveries on the level of Einstein and Newton.

7. Use the generating rules to make new predictions which can then be tested against the evidence of sensory experience.

The purpose of this final step is to complete the feedback loop with sensory experience in order to establish the usefulness of the model. There have no doubt been many models (in all fields of human endeavor) that have a beautiful theoretical structure and use precise mathematical or logical descriptions but that are impractical or inconsistent with sensory experience. It has been said that there is a fine line between genius and insanity. It is this feedback loop that separates someone with "big ideas" or a "fanciful imagination" from a genius. The genius can find his way back to the world or sensory experience, the schizophrenic and the "dreamer" get lost along the way.

Chapter 10

Conclusion

"'Education is that which remains, after one has forgotten everything he learned in school'."[1]

A fundamental belief of the model of Neuro-Linguistic Programming is that the *strategy* for how one thinks about information is as important as the *content* of the information. For example, when one knows the most effective strategy for learning how to spell, the learning of new spelling words becomes progressively easier. If one (as Einstein's statement above implies) forgets the content of what one has learned, what remains are the processes and strategies for *how* to think and learn. For NLP and for Einstein this is the most important part of learning. The strategy one uses to take in information determines how it is organized and put into use. As Einstein pointed out:

"The development of general ability for independent thinking and judgment should always be placed foremost, not the acquisition of special knowledge. If a person masters the fundamentals of his subject and has learned to think independently, he will surely find his way and besides will better be able to adapt himself to progress and changes than the person whose training principally consists in the acquiring of detailed knowledge."[2]

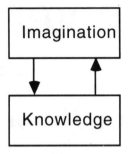

Einstein's comment reflects some of the core principles of effective learning. The mastery of fundamentals, the focus on process and the encouragement of independent thinking are the key abilities to adapt to progress and change. In addition to focusing on process and fundamentals, Einstein is saying that it is also important for individuals to learn strategies to think *for themselves* - to have their own independent thoughts and judgments. It was this ability that made Einstein a genius more so than specialized knowledge in the content area of physics. No doubt this is why Einstein claimed that *"imagination is more important than knowledge,"* and bemoaned the fact that schools put emphasis only on knowledge and not on the development of creative imagination and the celebration of independent thinking. (It is well known that Einstein did not do particularly well scholastically during his formal education). He went so far as to declare:

> *"It is, in fact, nothing short of a miracle that the modern methods of instruction have not yet entirely strangled the holy curiosity of inquiry."*[3]

Curiosity and inquiry are both the source and motivation for new knowledge and effective learning.

My purpose in studying Einstein's thought processes has been to (in the spirit of Einstein's own goals) illuminate some of the basic patterns that helped make Einstein who he was as a total person. As Einstein himself pointed out, it is the balanced development of the whole person that is the goal of education.

"The school should always have as its aim that the young man leave it as a harmonious personality, not as a specialist."[4]

While they are beyond the scope of this study, NLP provides numerous specific methods and exercises to develop many of the elements we have identified as being part of Einstein's basic thinking strategy. Perhaps if we cultivated some of these elements we have discovered about Einstein's strategy for **how** to think for ourselves in our young science students, there would be more potential Einsteins today.

In fact, some of these principles and strategies have been put into application within several school systems. Some years ago, for instance, my colleague, Todd Epstein, and I were involved in a project within the California School System called "Dynamic Assessment" in which we applied the kinds of strategies described in this book to help children who had been diagnosed with learning disabilities. The Dynamic Assessment program was designed for children of Hispanic origin who were non-native speakers of English and were found to have some kind of learning handicap. The purpose of the Dynamic Assessment program was to provide an alternative to the typical forms of the assessment and treatment of learning problems.

The school district in which it was implemented had a large Hispanic population, primarily from migrant working families. The learning problems among the Hispanic population had become so severe that the school district was in danger of losing its accreditation.

The idea of the Dynamic Assessment program was to assess the intelligence of the child, not on what he or she knew in response to test questions, as is typically done, but rather on the child's ability to 'learn how to learn' - that is, on how much progress the child could make in the process of learning. Instead of giving them a test, categorizing their disability and handing them their "life sentence", the special education teacher or psychologist was to interact with the students, coaching them as much as possible and trying to see how much progress could be made in a single session. We taught the teachers and psychologists how to elicit the micro-strategies of the students who were having problems and then just simply enrich, widen or add more choices to that strategy. The idea was to get the psychologists and teachers to think creatively along with the students in order to identify and expand the thought process the student was using in the problem area (they even attended one of my seminars on Einstein's strategy).

One great example of the success of this kind of approach was the case of a child who was three or four grade levels behind in math. The young Hispanic psychologist who was working with him made a brilliant intervention that I think characterizes the true spirit of Einstein's message.

In beginning the assessment process, the psychologist noticed that the boy was using the typical strategy of counting on his fingers to try to solve math problems. This strategy seemed to be slowing him down immensely and limiting his degree of performance.

A typical response in the classroom to such a situation is to reprimand the child, tell him not to count on his hands (in the old days the hands were slapped with a ruler), but offer no concrete or effective alternative.

Instead, the psychologist lead the boy to discover the limits of this strategy on his own and then to enrich the strategy by jumping outside of the typical presupposed limits of it.

"What is three plus two?" he asked.

- "One, two...three, four , Five!"

"Great!" the psychologist said. "What's thirteen plus four?"

"One, two, threeee....I don't know!"

Instead of telling him at that point that his strategy was wrong or ineffective, the psychologist tried to help the child think of a way to expand his strategy and be able to add thirteen plus four.

In the true spirit of Einstein the psychologist offered a suggestion. "I have an idea! Whatever the two numbers are, **you** always be the biggest number and count the smaller number out on your fingers. If it is thirteen plus four, then *you* are the thirteen. Now hold up four fingers and count."

-"Fourteen, fifteen, sixteen...seventeen!"

"Now, What is thirteen plus ten? Remember you be the bigger number." The child was able to add the two numbers.

"OK. What is a hundred and twenty five plus seven?" Initially the child hesitated. The numbers seemed so 'big'.

The psychologist reminded him, "You are the hundred twenty five. Now hold up seven fingers and count."

- "A hundred and thirty two!" came the delighted response.

Suddenly this child had made a quantum leap in the amount of numbers he could add by adding one simple step to his strategy. They went on from there to realize that even when you are adding columns of multi-digit numbers, if you learn to carry, you never have to add more than two numbers at a time. So this child who had never been able to add up numbers whose sum was higher than ten was suddenly doing multi-digit addition. His sense of excitement and self-esteem was tremendous.

Perhaps more important than his improved ability with math was the child's response to his mother when she asked him if he was happy that he had learned how to count.

He said, "I learned something a lot more important than that. I learned that I could learn how to learn! I can learn in different ways."

The amazing thing was this child's grades in all his other subjects began to improve too. And he became interested in other strategies for doing not only math but his other subjects.

This is a whole different approach to the process of teaching. It helps the student build confidence in his or her own learning abilities and to appreciate his or her own learning strategies. And on another level it builds the belief that there is more than one way to learn. This is not just the teacher's way or the way someone prescribed in a book, there are many ways of doing it.

I think there was something else that was subtle yet very important about having the child identify himself with the big numbers. "I am the big number". It is like Einstein identifying with his internal imagery.

The Dynamic Assessment program was very successful. The school district went from being one of the lowest in California to being second in the entire state. Naturally, this group of pioneers was thrilled with the kinds of breakthroughs they were getting. They decided to present what they were doing to other school districts and teachers.

But when they tried to share their techniques at educational conferences, they received strong resistance and antagonism. They couldn't understand it.

They said, "We didn't tell the other teachers that the way they were doing anything was wrong. We were just trying to let them know that there were other choices".

I said, "That is what you need to understand. In a culture that is concerned with finding the right answer and categorizing learning and learning problems into neat little categories, saying that there are lots of choices is probably more threatening than telling them they're wrong!"

The people who lived in Newton's nice little clockwork universe were incredibly threatened by Einstein's multiple-perspective world of relativity. If there are other choices, then there isn't any standard reality. If you have other choices you might lose your self-image. You won't see yourself in the mirror anymore. What is my identity? What is reality?

Einstein said, *"Great spirits are always opposed by mediocre minds."*

Whenever you change paradigms, even if you are just focusing on new tools or capabilities, these seemingly minor changes might lead to a whole different view of reality that may threaten the world views of others..

It is unfortunate that in many ways school systems are really not set up to teach people **how** to think. I've rarely, if ever, seen anybody ever get a good grade for how they thought about a problem. The grade isn't for how you thought about it, it is for what your answer was. If your answer matches the standard, then you must be smart. More often than not, tests are set up to sort or filter people out. Rather than being tested on your ability to think productively or creatively, you are getting tested on how well you understand and accept the values and presuppositions of the system.

One of the reasons they began the Dynamic Assessment program was because they discovered that many of the typical learning and intelligence tests were so full of cultural presuppositions that rather than measuring intelligence they were really measuring differences in cultural values.

As an example, a person came to several of my seminars who taught in a school on a Zuni Indian reservation in New Mexico. In the Zuni Indian's culture the collective is much more highly valued than individuals. Individual achievement is not valued in that culture as it is in the typical American culture. Instead, equality and the interests of the group are more highly valued.

For instance, after the second world war when the young men were returning from combat, rather than being welcomed back as triumphant warriors, the tribe members would not accept the soldiers back into the tribe until they had shared all of their experiences with all of the other members of the tribe so that no individuals would have any special knowledge that was unavailable to the others.

Unlike some native American tribes, the Zuni have a very low incidence of alcoholism, because being inebriated makes you act differently from everyone else - so it is not an acceptable form of dealing with problems. On the other hand, the Zuni have one of the highest incidents of suicide of Native American Cultures; because it is the only remaining means of escape from the cultural binds in which they are finding themselves.

As an example of such a bind, the person who was teaching the Zunis pointed out that the US government had just taken the standard American school system and tried to impose it into that culture and it was creating a lot problems. As part of standard curriculum, for example, students were given an assignment to write about their personal strengths. Instead of writing about themselves, they wrote about their families and their tribe but never their own individual achievements. When they were given their report cards, nineteen out of twenty were left on the desks in the classroom because grades made people unequal.

The presupposition in typical Western and certainly American culture is that somehow grades are a reward that will motivate students (or if negative will motivate parents) to put effort into learning. But this backfired with the Zuni. When the name of a student who did well in a subject was put on public display on the honor roll it was torn off the page and the next semester that student's grades would go down.

There are all kinds of presupposed values in our approach to education. Unfortunately, most of them are not about how to think, but about how to behave.

There is a classic example or this type of cultural presupposition in *The One Minute Manager.* The authors give this example about someone who goes to speak to his child's teacher because the child is having some problems at school. In his discussions with the teacher he points out that as a manager it is important for the company to make sure that all of his subordinates are successful in their tasks. And that he has found that if he gives them clear goals and evidence procedures they perform better. He then makes the suggestion to the teacher that maybe he should give the children the questions for the final test at the beginning of the semester, so they would know what was going to be important from the class, and would know what to study for.

The teacher was appalled and flabbergasted. He said, "I can't do that. Then *everybody* would get an A!"

In other words, if everyone is successful how do you separate them out? How do you know who is going to be the doctor or the mechanic? That is a presupposition which is deeply embedded in our culture.

You can imagine that somebody like Hitler would have found it the most threatening idea in the world that we didn't have to have a superior race. If there is no superior and inferior, if there is no scarcity of intellectual and physical resources, how do we know who we are? How *do* we organize society?

I pointed out to our research group that when you start suggesting that there are other ways of doing math, that there are choices, you hear, "Hey this guy has gone completely off his rocker, and he is out there on his light beam! Math produces only one right answer. There must be only one right way to do it."

Change is going to create instability. Moving on the light beam is going to threaten the person sitting on the asteroid. So the person sitting on the asteroid says, "That is just a dream! You are being silly. Not everybody can get an A. Not *everybody* can be genius."

And the one on the light beam says, "No, no. I'll prove to you that this is real. I can really affect people. I'm not lying, I'm not a charlatan."

And you find a funny thing. The more he can actually demonstrate the validity of his point of view, the more resistance he gets.

This is because the real issue is that this new way of looking at reality is a challenge to the person's whole model of the world, and a challenge to his or her sense of coherence.

Whose frame of reference is the true reality? When Galileo first suggested that the Earth was not the center of the universe he was imprisoned, excommunicated and threatened with death. All the proof he had just made things worse!

If everybody could be a genius, how will anyone be special or be superior? How will we know whom to look up to? You can't have a whole corporation of leaders. How shall we differentiate ourselves? What will identity be, if it is not hierarchical? How will we structure our governments and organizations, as well as our systems of reward and punishment?

I think that becomes the real issue.

I pointed out to our group of teachers and psychologists that they had to realize how potentially subversive their message really was - just like Einstein's. They were saying that if somebody is smarter than you, if they excel, you don't have to feel like less of a person. You don't have to feel threatened by somebody who does something better than you because you have a technology that allows you to model it. You have a technology to acknowledge and enrich your abilities.

If this child is good at sports and I am good at math, I don't have to be afraid of that one and make him my enemy and make a differentiation between jocks and intellectuals. As Einstein said, the fact that people have a different model of the world is not threatening, it is an opportunity to be enriched. The fact that somebody thinks differently from me, is not a reason for ostracizing them. But it is a great opportunity to enlarge my model of the world.

That belief system itself is really threatening to many people. Nazi intellectuals and physicists wrote many articles debunking Einstein's theory of relativity and his books were burned.

So the main question for the research team was, "How do we deal with this, then? What do we do?"

Here again we can draw upon the guidance of Einstein's genius. First of all, it is a trap to align yourself with one or the other points of view. Einstein could have just stayed up in the light beam and said, "You are wrong. To heck with you! And Newton was an idiot."

Instead he said, "No, no. I must know what it is like to be in this resistant frame of reference, to be in 'second position'. But that must not stop me from maintaining the validity of my own frame of reference. And as soon as I find the fundamental presupposition that creates the impasse, then I have to shift to a higher level position and ask, 'What is the same in all the frames of reference?'" If the universe is indeed a "friendly place", there must be something fundamental; something deeper than either frame of reference that unites them. What are "God's thoughts" on the matter?

Putting themselves in the perspective of the resistance teachers, our team members began to uncover some of the limiting assumptions that were behind that resistance. For instance, a primary concern of classroom teachers was, "I have forty or fifty students in a class, I can't teach each of them according to their individual learning style." Of course, the presupposition was that *the teacher* had to teach all of the children according to their individual styles. Why couldn't the students teach each other? Knowledge about *how to* learn is not the exclusive property of the teacher. How many young Einsteins are there in classrooms around the world?

This line of questioning led to the next assumption; "The students can't teach each other because they don't have the information." The presupposition in this case was that students could not teach each other because they lacked the 'content'. The next question was, "Why can't the students teach each other *how* to learn, and the teacher can provide *what* to learn?" As it turned out, in fact, the most effective spelling teacher in the entire school district was an eleven year old girl. She could teach anyone to spell, and enjoyed doing it.

By continuing to take all the different points of view, the psychologists and teachers eventually realized that the primary conflict of values was between "support" and "empowerment".

In one frame of reference the belief was that, if a child has a learning problem, we have to diagnose this learning problem, and change our expectations about what that child is capable of and provide him with the support he needs in order to function. It is unfair and cruel to the child to expect more out of him than he is capable of.

In the other frame of reference the belief was that it was also unfair and cruel to build the belief in the child that she was incapable of learning for the rest of her life by labeling her "disabled" - especially if you had not explored all of the avenues and possibilities that might empower the child to grow and to think for herself.

As we continued to look for the presuppositions in the statements, it became pretty obvious that they were both based on fairness and cruelty to the child - but the child's perspective was missing! They were both seeing through the eyes of the teachers not the child. And certainly, the child is "the source" of the adult, whether that adult is an educator, psychologist, manager, mother, etc.

The researchers began presenting the results of their research to their colleagues from the *child's* perspective and the resistance disappeared. They got their audience to *identify* with the child - to go to second position with the child. Not only did it fill in an important point of view that had been missing, it put the audience in a frame of reference where they were naturally more curious and open.

Furthermore, they realized that support and empowerment were not incompatible. They began exploring an "optimal learning environment" - one that provided both support and empowerment. The classroom had psychologists and teachers sharing the same space (most often a school psychologist never sees the student in the context of the classroom). They also discovered that, given the right "how to" technology, students could teach each other more effectively in many cases than teachers could. (As I mentioned earlier, the most effective spelling teacher in their school district was an eleven year old girl.) They began implementing cooperative learning programs, where students shared their learning strategies with each other.

They even found that students who had "behavior problems" because they were constantly talking and sharing information with other children in the standard classroom, became positive catalysts for change when they were given permission to learn cooperatively (due to their high degree of relational skills).

Not only did these teachers find their ideas becoming more accepted, the woman who spearheaded the project in that school system was appointed to review educational legislation for the entire state.

We find these kinds of issues happening in any field where change is taking place.

In my work in the area of belief systems and health, I run into similarly conflicting frames of reference. Some medical people are of the belief that, "It is all in the body. Only physical interventions like surgery and medicine cause healing to happen, and it is ridiculous to think that there is anything going on in the mind that is really involved. Come back off that light beam."

But I also find alternative health practitioners who say "No, the mind is the only source of change. You must exert your mind over the body. Your thoughts create illness."

To me these are just the two halves of the same kind of thinking: linear, cause-effect, deterministic thinking. The issue is not whether the cause of healing is in the mind or in the body. The deeper issue is to challenge the presuppositions of linear Newtonian thinking in biology and move to a more systemic model that deals with the commonalities of both mind and body, neurology and immune system, etc.

Both of these issues point to the need for the constant re-evaluation of the presuppositions behind our thinking.

As Einstein pointed out:

> *"Sometimes one sees in the school simply the instrument for transferring a certain maximum quantity of knowledge to the growing generation. But that is not right. Knowledge is dead; the school, however, serves the living."*[5]

The results of Einstein's impressive mental strategies and processes stand as a monument to him today. Yet, as he himself pointed out, the result of the process of finding truth is not the goal. Rather, the ultimate purpose of learning is the transfer of the process itself.

> *"[W]ith the affairs of active human beings... knowledge of truth alone does not suffice; on the contrary this knowledge must continually be renewed by ceaseless effort, if it is not to be lost. It resembles a statue of marble which stands in the desert and is continuously threatened with burial by the shifting sand. The hands of service must ever be at work, in order that the marble continue to shine in the sun. To these serving hands mine shall also belong."* [6]

I hope that this study of Einstein has helped to push aside at least a few grains of sand from covering up the name of Albert Einstein.

In the words of Einstein himself, we might at this point ask:

> *"Is there not a certain satisfaction in the fact that natural limits are set to the life of the individual, so that at its conclusion it may appear as a work of art?"*[7]

By any standard, the life of Albert Einstein shines as one of the masterpieces of human history.

Footnotes to Chapter 10

1. Albert Einstein, *"On Education,"* **Out of My Later Years**, The Citadel Press, Secaucus, New Jersey, 1956, p. 36.

2. Albert Einstein, *"On Education,"* p. 36.

3. Albert Einstein, *"Autobiographical Notes,"* **Albert Einstein, Philosopher-Scientist** by Paul Arthur Schilpp, Northwestern University Press, Evanston, Ill., 1949, p. 17.

4. Albert Einstein, *"On Education,"* p. 36.

5. Albert Einstein, *"On Education,"* p. 32.

6. Albert Einstein, *"On Education,"* p. 31-32.

7. **ALBERT EINSTEIN,** Pomegranate Calendars & Books, Corte Madera, CA, 1986, p. 24.

Afterword

I hope you have enjoyed this exploration into the *Strategies of Genius*. As I indicated during the course of the book, many tools and resources exist to further develop and apply the models, strategies and skills described within these pages. In addition to the tools already mentioned, I am currently planning a collection of tapes, workbooks, computer software and multi media programs to help illustrate and support the types of strategies described in this book. I am also conducting seminars and workshops on *Strategies of Genius* in various parts of the United States and Europe as well as training programs on the applications of NLP for Creativity, Health, Leadership, Effective Presentations Skills, and Modeling.

If you would like to receive further information regarding these tools and resources or any future developments related to *Strategies of Genius*, please contact:

Strategies of Genius
P.O. Box 67448
Scotts Valley, California 95067-7448
Phone & Fax: (408) 438-8314

Appendix A:
Background and
Principles of NLP

NLP was originated by John Grinder (whose background was in linguistics) and Richard Bandler (whose background was in mathematics and gestalt therapy) for the purpose of making explicit models of human excellence. Their first work *The Structure of Magic Vol. I & II* (1975, 1976) identified the verbal and behavioral patterns of therapists Fritz Perls (the creator of gestalt therapy) and Virginia Satir (internationally renowned family therapist). Their next work *Patterns of the Hypnotic Techniques of Milton H. Erickson, M.D. Vol. I & II* (1975, 1976) examined the verbal and behavioral patterns of Milton Erickson, founder of the American Society of Clinical Hypnosis and one of the most widely acknowledged and clinically successful psychiatrists of our times.

As a result of this earlier work, Grinder and Bandler formalized their modeling techniques and their own individual contributions under the name "Neuro-Linguistic Programming" to symbolize the relationship between the brain, language and the body. The basics of this model has been described in a series of books including *Frogs Into Princes* (Bandler & Grinder, 1979), *Neuro-Linguistic Programming Vol. I* (Dilts, Grinder, Bandler, DeLozier, 1980), *Reframing* (Bandler & Grinder, 1982) and *Using Your Brain* (Bandler, 1985).

In essence, all of NLP is founded on two fundamental premises:

1. *The Map is Not the Territory.* As human beings, we can never know reality. We can only know our perceptions of reality. We experience and respond to the world around us primarily through our sensory representational systems. It is our 'neuro-linguistic' maps of reality that determine how we behave and that give those behaviors meaning, not reality itself. It is generally not reality that limits us or empowers us, but rather our map of reality.

2. *Life and 'Mind' are Systemic Processes.* The processes that take place within a human being and between human beings and their environment are systemic. Our bodies, our societies, and our universe form an ecology of complex systems and subsystems all of which interact with and mutually influence each other. It is not possible to completely isolate any part of the system from the rest of the system. Such systems are based on certain 'self-organizing' principles and naturally seek optimal states of balance or homeostasis.

According to NLP, the basic process of change involves 1) finding out what the *present state* of the person is, and 2) adding the appropriate *resources* to lead that person to 3) the *desired state*.

Present State + Appropriate Resources —> Desired State

The distinctions and techniques of NLP are organized to help identify and define present states and desired states of various types and levels and then to access and apply the appropriate resources to produce effective and ecological change in the direction of the desired state.

The Nervous System

Higher organisms coordinate their behavior and organize their experience of the world through their nervous systems. In human beings, the nervous system may be viewed as consisting of three primary subsystems: 1) the Central Nervous System 2) the Peripheral Nervous System and 3) the Autonomic Nervous System.

The *Central Nervous System* is made up of the brain and spinal cord. It controls our muscles and movement and is associated with conscious thought and action.

The *Peripheral Nervous System* is made up of the branches of the spinal cord and the sense organs. It relays information about the environment from the organs, muscles and glands to the central nervous system and back again.

The *Autonomic Nervous System* deals with a network of nerves outside of the spinal cord that deals with many unconscious activities such as temperature regulation, circulation, salivation, the initiation of the "fight-flight" reaction and other emotional and attentional states.

The Central Nervous System executes mental programs, plans and strategies via the Peripheral Nervous System. The Autonomic Nervous System determines the state of the biological "hardware" within which those programs are carried out. While most people are consciously aware of their sensations, thoughts and actions, the functions of the Autonomic Nervous System generally take place outside of conscious awareness.

Whether it be talking, thinking, eating, understanding, working or sleeping; all human action and experiences are mediated and manifested through the interplay of these three parts of the nervous system. Learning is a function of the establishment of coherent patterns of organization and interaction within these three neurological subsystems.

The Fundamental Structure of Behavior: T.O.T.E. Model

A mental strategy is typically organized into a basic feedback loop called a T.O.T.E. (Miller, et al, 1960). The letters **T.O.T.E.** stand for *Test-Operate-Test-Exit*. The T.O.T.E. concept maintains that all mental and behavioral programs revolve around having a *fixed goal* and a *variable means to achieve that goal*. This model indicates that, as we think, we set goals in our mind (consciously or unconsciously) and develop a TEST for when that goal has been achieved. If that goal is not achieved we OPERATE to change something or do something to get closer to our goal. When our TEST criteria have been satisfied we then EXIT on to the next step.

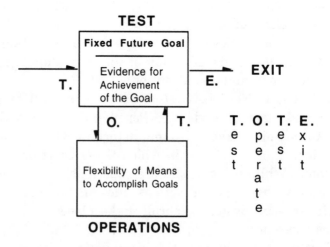

So the function of any particular part of a behavioral program could be to (**T**)est information from the senses in order to check progress towards the goal or to (**O**)perate to change some part of the ongoing experience so that it can satisfy the (**T**)est and (**E**)xit on to the next part of the program.

For example, one TEST for creativity might be that an idea is "unique". If the concept you have come up with is not unique enough you will OPERATE or go through a procedure to make the idea more unique or to come up with a better concept.

According to the T.O.T.E. model, effective performance comes from:

1. Having a fixed future goal.

2. Having the sensory evidence necessary to accurately determine your progress toward the goal.

3. Having a variable set of means to get to your goal and the behavioral flexibility to implement these choices.

Perceptual Positions

Perceptual positions refer to the fundamental points of view you can take concerning a relationship between yourself and another person.

1st Position: Associated in your own point of view, beliefs and assumptions, seeing the external world through your own eyes. Use first person language when talking about yourself - "I am seeing," "I feel," etc.

2nd Position: Associated in another person's point of view, beliefs and assumptions, seeing the external world through his or her eyes. Use second person language when talking about your self in first position - "You are", "You look," etc.

3rd Position: Associated in a point of view outside of the relationship between yourself and the other person with the beliefs and assumptions from both 1st and 2nd position. Use third person language when talking about yourself in first position or the other person (2nd position) - "He is," "She says," "They are," etc.

Meta Position: Associated in a 3rd position but with the beliefs and assumptions from only one of the other perceptual positions.

Observer Position: Associated in a 3rd position but suspending any beliefs and assumptions from 1st and 2nd position.

Levels of Processing and Organization

People often talk about responding to things on different *"levels"*. For instance, someone might say that some experience was negative on one level but positive on another level. In our brain structure, language, and perceptual systems there are natural hierarchies or levels of experience. The effect of each level is to organize and control the information on the level below it. Changing something on an upper level would necessarily change things on the lower levels; changing something on a lower level could but would not necessarily effect the upper levels. Anthropologist Gregory Bateson identified four basic levels of learning and change - each level more abstract than the level below it but each having a greater degree of impact on the individual. These levels roughly correspond to:

* *Environmental factors* determine the external opportunities or constraints a person has to react to. Answer to the questions **where?** and **when?**

* *Behavior* is made up of specific actions or reactions within the environment. Answer to the question **what?**

* *Capabilities* guide and give direction to behavioral actions through a mental map, plan or strategy. Answer to the question **how?**

* *Beliefs* and *values* provide the reinforcement (motivation and permission) that supports or denies capabilities. Answer to the question **why?**

* *Identity* factors determine overall purpose (mission) and shape beliefs and values through our sense of self. Answer to the question **who?**

* *Spiritual* issues relate to the fact that we are a part of a larger system that reaches beyond ourselves as individuals to our family, community and global systems. Answer to the question **who else?**

The environment level involves the specific external conditions in which our behavior takes place. Behaviors without any inner map, plan or strategy to guide them, however, are like knee jerk reactions, habits or rituals. At the level of capability we are able to select, alter and adapt a class of behaviors to a wider set of external situations. At the level of beliefs and values we may encourage, inhibit or generalize a particular strategy, plan or way of thinking.   Identity, of course, consolidates whole systems of beliefs and values into a sense of self. While each level becomes more abstracted from the specifics of behavior and sensory experience, it actually has more and more widespread effect on our behavior and experience.

"Neuro-Logical" Levels

Each of these processes involves a different level of organization and mobilizes successively deeper mobilization and commitment of neurological 'circuitry'.

Spiritual -*Holographic* - Nervous system as a whole.

A. Identity - *Immune system and endocrine system* - Deep life sustaining functions.
B. Beliefs -*Autonomic nervous system* (e.g. heart rate, pupil dilation, etc.) - Unconscious responses.
C. Capabilities - *Cortical systems* - Semi conscious actions (eye movements, posture, etc.)
D.   Behaviors - *Motor system (pyramidal & cerebellum)* - Conscious actions
E. Environment - *Peripheral nervous system* - Sensations and reflex reactions.

Cognitive Patterns: The R.O.L.E. Model

The goal of the R.O.L.E. modeling process is to identify the essential elements of thinking and behavior used to produce a particular response or outcome. This involves identifying the critical steps of the mental strategy and the role each step plays in the overall neurological "program". This role is determined by the following four factors which are indicated by the letters which make up the name of the **R.O.L.E.** Model - *Representational Systems; Orientation; Links; Effect.*

Representational **Systems** have to do with which of the five senses are most dominant for the particular mental step in the strategy: **V**isual (sight), **A**uditory (sound), **K**inesthetic (feeling), **O**lfactory (smell), **G**ustatory (taste).

Each representational system is designed to perceive certain basic qualities of the experiences it senses. These include characteristics such as *color, brightness, tone, loudness, temperature, pressure,* etc. These qualities are called "submodalities" in NLP since they are subcomponents of each of the representational systems.

Orientation has to do with whether a particular sensory representation is focused (**e**)xternally toward the outside world or (**i**)nternally toward either (**r**)emembered or (**c**)onstructed experiences. For instance, when you are seeing something, is it in the outside world, in memory or in your imagination?

Links have to do with how a particular step or sensory representation is linked to the other representations. For example, is something seen in the external environment linked to internal feelings, remembered images, or words? Is a particular feeling linked to constructed pictures, memories of sounds or other feelings?

There are two basic ways that representations can be linked together: sequentially and simultaneously. Sequential links act as *anchors* or triggers such that one representation follows another in a linear chain of events.

Simultaneous links occur as what are called *synesthesias.* Synesthesia links have to do with the ongoing overlap between sensory representations. Certain qualities of feelings may be linked to certain qualities of imagery - for example, visualizing the shape of a sound or hearing a color.

Certainly, both of these kinds of links are essential to thinking, learning, creativity and the general organization of our experiences.

Effect has to do with the result, effect or purpose of each step in the thought process. For instance, the function of the step could be to generate or input a sensory representation, to test or evaluate a particular sensory representation or to operate to change some part of an experience or behavior in relation to the goal.

Physiological Clues: Making the R.O.L.E. into a B.A.G.E.L.

The R.O.L.E. model elements deal primarily with cognitive processes.   In order to function, however, these mental programs need the help of certain bodily and physiological processes for consolidation and expression. These physical reactions are important for the teaching or development of certain mental processes as well as for the external observation and confirmation of them.   The primary behavioral elements involved in R.O.L.E. modeling are:

> **B**ody Posture.
> **A**ccessing cues
> **G**estures.
> **E**ye movements.
> **L**anguage Patterns.

1. Body Posture

People often assume systematic, habitual postures when deep in thought. These postures can indicate a great deal about the representational system the person is using. The following are some typical examples:

   a. **Visual:** *Leaning back with head and shoulders up or rounded, shallow breathing*

   b. **Auditory:** *Body leaning forward, head cocked, shoulders back, arms folded.*

   c. **Kinesthetic:** *Head and shoulders down, deep breathing.*

2. Accessing Cues

When people are thinking, they cue or trigger certain types
of representations in a number of different ways including:
breathing rate, non-verbal "grunts and groans", facial ex-
pressions, snapping their fingers, scratching their heads, and
so on. Some of these cues are idiosyncratic to the individual
and need to be 'calibrated' to a particular person. Many of
these cues, however, are associated with particular sensory
processes"

a. **Visual:** *High shallow breathing, squinting eyes, voice
higher pitch and faster tempo.*

b. **Auditory:** *Diaphragmatic breathing, knitted brow, fluctuating voice tone and tempo.*

c. **Kinesthetic:** *Deep abdominal breathing, deep breathy
voice in a slower tempo.*

3. Gestures.

People will often touch, point to or use gestures indicating
the sense organ they are using to think with. Some typical
examples include:

a. **Visual:** *Touching or pointing to the eyes; gestures made
above eye level.*

b. **Auditory:** *Pointing toward or gesturing near the ears;
touching the mouth or jaw.*

c. **Kinesthetic:** *Touching the chest and stomach area;
gestures made below the neck.*

4. Eye movements

Automatic, unconscious eye movements often accompany particular thought processes indicating the accessing of one of the representational systems. NLP has categorized these cues into the following pattern:

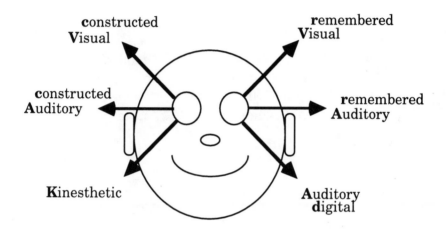

constructed
Visual

remembered
Visual

constructed
Auditory

remembered
Auditory

Kinesthetic

Auditory
digital

NLP Eye Movement Patterns

5. Language Patterns

A primary method of Neuro-Linguistic analysis is to search for particular linguistic patterns, such as 'predicates', which indicate a particular neurological representational system or sub-modality, and how that system or quality is being used in the overall program of thought. Predicates are words, such as verbs, adverbs and adjectives, which indicate actions or qualities as opposed to things. This type of language is typically selected at an unconscious level and thus reflects the underlying unconscious structure which produced them. The following is a list of common sensory based predicates:

VISUAL	AUDITORY	KINESTHETIC
"see"	"hear"	"grasp"
"look"	"listen"	"touch"
"sight"	"sound"	"feeling"
"clear"	"resonant"	"solid"
"bright"	"loud"	"heavy"
"picture"	"word"	"handle"
"hazy"	'noisy"	"rough"
"brings to light"	"rings a bell"	"connects"
"show"	"tell"	"move

Internal States

NLP focuses on identifying, using and changing patterns in the thought processes and physiology that influence people's behavior as a means of improving the quality and effectiveness of their performance. The basic premise of NLP is that the human brain functions similarly to a computer - by executing "programs" or mental strategies that are composed of ordered sequences of instructions or internal representations. Certain programs or strategies function better for accomplishing certain tasks than others, and it is the strategy that an individual uses that will to a great extent determine whether his performance is one of mediocrity or excellence.

The efficacy and ability to carry out a particular mental program is to a large degree determined by the physiological state of the individual. Clearly, if a computer has a bad chip or power surges in its electrical supply its programs will not be able to execute effectively. The same is true for the human brain. The level of arousal, receptivity, stress, etc., of the individual will determine how effectively he can carry out his own mental programs. Heart rate, breathing rate, body posture, blood pressure, muscle tension, reaction time and galvanic skin response are examples of physical measures that effect and accompany changes in overall physiological state. NLP uses these measures to identify, model and train physiological states of excellence in individuals so that these states may be purposefully reproduced and used to achieve optimal performance.

Thus, an individual's internal state has important influences on his or her ability to perform in any situation.

Anchoring

Anchoring is a process that on the surface is similar to the "conditioning" technique used by Pavlov to create a link between the hearing of a bell and salivation in dogs. By associating the sound of a bell with the act of giving food to his dogs, Pavlov found he could eventually just ring the bell and the dogs would start salivating, even though no food was given. In the behaviorist's stimulus-response conditioning formula, however, the stimulus is always an environmental cue and the response is always a specific behavioral action. The association is considered reflexive and not a matter of choice.

In NLP the term *"anchoring"* refers to the establishment of links between R.O.L.E. Model elements and has been expanded to include other logical levels than environment and behavior. A remembered picture may become an anchor for a particular internal feeling, for instance. A touch on the leg may become an anchor for a visual fantasy or even a belief. A voice tone may become an anchor for a state of excitement or confidence. A person may consciously choose to establish and retrigger these associations for himself. Rather than being a mindless knee-jerk reflex, an anchor becomes a tool for self empowerment. Obviously, anchoring can be a very useful tool for helping to establish and reactivate the mental processes associated with creativity.

Most often anchors may be established through simply associating two experiences together in time. In behavioral conditioning models, associations become more strongly established through repetition. Repetition may also be used to strengthen anchors as well. For example, you could ask someone to vividly reexperience a time that she was very creative and pat her shoulder while she is thinking of the experience. If you repeat this once or twice the pat on shoulder will begin to become linked to the creative state. Eventually a pat on the shoulder will automatically remind the person of the creative state.

Strategies

1. Definition of *"Strategy"* :
  a. From the Greek word *"strategos"* meaning *"general."*

  b. *"A detailed plan for reaching a goal or advantage."* (Random House Dictionary)

  c. In NLP, the term *"strategy"* is used to mean the steps of a mental process or program (in the sense of a computer program) that leads to a particular goal or outcome. Each step in the strategy is characterized by the use of one of the five senses or *"representational systems."*

2. Classes of Strategies
  a. Memory
  b. Decision Making
  c. Learning
  d. Creativity
  e. Motivation
  f. Reality
  g. Belief (or Convincer)

3. Strategy Procedures
  a. Elicitation
  b. Utilization
  c. Design
  d. "Installation" - Reorganization

4. Structure of a Strategy
  a. General Systems Model

b. NLP Strategy Structure

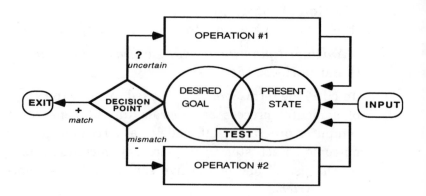

Appendix B:
Presuppositions of NLP

The Map is not the Territory

1. People respond to their own perceptions of reality.

2. Every person has their own individual map of the world. No individual map of the world is any more "real" or "true" than any other.

3. The meaning of a communication to another person is the response it elicits in that person, regardless of the intent of the communicator.

4. The 'wisest' and most 'compassionate' maps are those which make available the widest and richest number of choices, as opposed to being the most "real" or "accurate".

5. People already have (or potentially have) all of the resources they need to act effectively.

6. People make the best choices available to them given possibilities and the capabilities that they perceive available to them from their model of the world. Any behavior no matter how evil, crazy or bizarre it seems is the best choice available to the person at that point in time - if given a more appropriate choice (within the context of their model of the world) the person will be more likely to take it.

7. Change comes from releasing the appropriate resource, or activating the potential resource, for a particular context by enriching a person's map of the world.

Life And 'Mind' Are Systemic Processes

1. The processes that take place within a person, and between people and their environment, are systemic. Our bodies, our societies and our universe form an ecology of systems and subsystems all of which interact with and mutually influence each other.

2. It is not possible to completely isolate any part of a system from the rest of the system. People cannot not influence each other. Interactions between people form feedback loops - such that a person will be effected by the results that their own actions have on other people.

3. Systems are 'self organizing' and naturally seek states of balance and stability. There are no failures, only feedback.

4. No response, experience or behavior is meaningful outside of the context in which it was established or the response it elicits next. Any behavior, experience or response may serve as a resource or limitation depending on how it fits in with the rest of the system.

5. Not all interactions in a system are on the same level. What is positive on one level may be negative on another level. It is useful to separate behavior from "self" - to separate the positive intent, function, belief, etc. that generates the behavior from the behavior itself.

6. At some level all behavior is (or at one time was) "positively intended". It is or was perceived as appropriate given the context in which it was established, from the point of view of the person whose behavior it is. It is easier and more productive to respond to the intention rather than the expression of a problematic behavior.

7. Environments and contexts change. The same action will not always produce the same result.   In order to successfully adapt and survive, a member of a system needs to have a certain amount of flexibility.   That amount of flexibility has to be proportional to the variation in the rest of the system. As a system becomes more complex, more flexibility is required.

8. If what you are doing is not getting the response you want then keep varying your behavior until you do elicit the response.

Appendix C:
Glossary of NLP Terminology

ACCESSING CUES - Subtle behaviors that will both help to trigger and indicate which representational system a person is using to think with. Typical types of accessing cues include *eye movements, voice tone and tempo, body posture, gestures and breathing patterns.*

ANCHORING - The process of associating an internal response with some *external trigger* (similar to classical conditioning) so that the response may be quickly, and sometimes covertly, reaccessed.

AUDITORY - Relating to *hearing* or the sense of hearing.

BEHAVIOR - The specific physical actions and reactions through which we interact with the people and environment around us.

BEHAVIORAL FLEXIBILITY - The ability to vary one's own behavior in order to elicit or secure a response from another person.

BELIEFS - Closely held generalizations about 1) cause, 2) meaning and 3) boundaries in the (a) world around us, (b) our behavior, (c) our capabilities of and our (d) identities. Beliefs function at a different level than concrete reality and serve to guide and interpret our perceptions of reality often by connecting them to our criteria or value systems. Beliefs are notoriously difficult to change through typical rules of logic or rational thinking.

CALIBRATION - The process of learning to read another person's unconscious, non-verbal responses in an ongoing interaction by pairing observable behavioral cues with a specific internal response.

CALIBRATED LOOP - Unconscious pattern of communication in which behavioral cues of one person triggers specific responses from another person in an ongoing interaction.

CAPABILITY - Mastery over an entire class of behavior - knowing **HOW TO** do something. Capabilities come from the development of a mental map that allows us to select and organize groups of individual behaviors. In NLP these mental maps take the form of cognitive strategies and maps.

CHUNKING - Organizing or breaking down some experience into bigger or smaller pieces. *"Chunking up"* involves moving to a larger, more abstract level of information. *"Chunking down"* involves moving to a more specific and concrete level of information. *"Chunking laterally"* involves finding other examples at the same level of information.

CONGRUENCE - When all of a person's internal beliefs, strategies and behaviors are fully in agreement and oriented toward securing a desired outcome.

CONTEXT - The framework surrounding a particular event. This framework will often determine how a particular experience or event is interpreted.

CRITERIA - The values or standards a person uses to make decisions and judgments.

DEEP STRUCTURE - The neurological maps (both conscious and unconscious) that people use to organize and guide their behavior.

ENVIRONMENT - The external context in which our behavior takes place. Our environment is that which we perceive as being "outside" of us. It is not part of our behavior but is rather something we must react to.

FOUR TUPLE (or **4-tuple**) - A shorthand method used to notate the structure of any particular experience. The concept of the four tuple maintains that any experience must be composed of some combination of the four primary representational classes - <A,V,K,O> - where A = *auditory, V = visual, K = kinesthetic, and O = olfactory / gustatory.*

FUTURE PACING - The process of *mentally rehearsing* oneself through some future situation in order to help insure that the desired behavior will occur naturally and automatically.

GUSTATORY - Relating to *taste* or the sense of taste.

IDENTITY - Our sense of who we are. Our sense of identity organizes our beliefs, capabilities and behaviors into a single system.

INSTALLATION - The process of facilitating the acquisition of a new strategy or behavior. A new strategy may be installed through some combination of anchoring, accessing cues, metaphor and futurepacing.

KINESTHETIC - relates to *body sensations.* In NLP the term kinesthetic is used to encompass all kinds of feelings including *tactile, visceral* and *emotional.*

LOGICAL LEVELS - An internal hierarchy of organization in which each level is progressively more psychologically encompassing and impactful. In order of importance (from high to low) these levels include 1) identity, 2) beliefs, 3) capabilities, 4) behavior and 5) environment.

META MODEL - A model developed by John Grinder and Richard Bandler that identifies categories of language patterns that can be problematic or ambiguous.

META PROGRAM - A level of mental programming that determines how we sort, orient to, and chunk our experiences. Our meta programs are more abstract than our specific strategies for thinking and define our general approach to a particular issue rather than the details of our thinking process.

METAPHOR - The process of thinking about one situation or phenomena as something else, i.e. *stories, parables* and *analogies*.

MODELING - The process of observing and mapping the successful behaviors of other people.

NEURO-LINGUISTIC PROGRAMMING (NLP) - A behavioral model and set of explicit skills and techniques founded by John Grinder and Richard Bandler in 1975. Defined as *the study of the structure of subjective experience.* NLP studies the patterns or *"programming"* created by the interaction between the brain (*"neuro"*), language (*"linguistic"*) and the body, that produce both effective and ineffective behavior in order to better understand the processes behind human excellence. The skills and techniques were derived by observing the patterns of excellence in experts from diverse fields of professional communication including psychotherapy, business, health and education.

OLFACTORY - Relating to *smell* or the sense of smell.

OUTCOMES - Goals or desired states that a person or organization aspires to achieve.

PACING - A method used by communicators to quickly establish *rapport* by matching certain aspects of their behavior to those of the person with whom they are communicating - a *matching* or *mirroring* of behavior.

PARTS - A metaphorical way of talking about independent programs and strategies of behavior. Programs or "parts" will often develop a persona that becomes one of their identifying features.

PERCEPTUAL POSITIONS - A particular perspective or point of view. In NLP there are three basic positions one can take in perceiving a particular experience. *First position* involves experiencing something through our own eyes *associated* in a first person point of view. *Second position* involves experiencing something as if we were in another person's 'shoes'. *Third position* involves standing back and perceiving the relationship between ourselves and others from an observer's perspective.

PREDICATES - Process words (like *verbs, adverbs* and *adjectives*) that a person selects to describe a subject. Predicates are used in NLP to identify which *representational system* a person is using to process information.

QUOTES - A pattern in which a message that you want to deliver can be embedded in quotations, as if someone else had stated the message.

RAPPORT - The establishment of *trust, harmony* and *cooperation* in a relationship.

REFRAMING - A process used in NLP through which a problematic behavior is separated from the *positive intention* of the internal program or "part" that is responsible for the behavior. New choices of behavior are established by having the part responsible for the old behavior take responsibility for implementing other behaviors that satisfy the same positive intention but don't have the problematic by-products.

REPRESENTATIONAL SYSTEMS - the five senses: *seeing, hearing, touching (feeling), smelling, and tasting.*

REPRESENTATIONAL SYSTEM PRIMACY - Where an individual systematically uses one sense over the other to process and organize his or her experience. Primary representational system will determine many personality traits as well as learning capabilities.

SECONDARY GAIN - Where some seemingly negative or problematic behavior actually carries out some *positive function* at some other level. For example, smoking may help a person to relax or help them fit a particular self image.

STATE - The total ongoing mental and physical conditions from which a person is acting.

STRATEGY - A set of explicit mental and behavioral steps used to achieve a specific outcome. In NLP, the most important aspect of a strategy is considered to be the representational systems used to carry out the specific steps.

SUBMODALITIES - Submodalities are the special sensory qualities perceived by each of the senses. For example, visual submodalities include *color, shape, movement, brightness, depth, etc.,* auditory submodalities include *volume, pitch, tempo, etc.,* and kinesthetic submodalities include such qualities as *pressure, temperature, texture, location, etc.*

SURFACE STRUCTURE - The *words* or *language* used to describe or stand for the actual primary sensory representations stored in the brain.

SYNESTHESIA - The process of *overlap* between representational systems, characterized by phenomena like *"see-feel circuits,"* in which a person derives feelings from what he or she sees, and *"hear-feel circuits,"* in which a person gets feelings from what he or she hears. Any two sensory modalities may be linked together.

T.O.T.E. - Developed by Miller, Galanter and Pribram, the term stands for the sequence *Test-Operate-Test-Exit,* which describes the basic feedback loop used to guide all behavior.

TRANSDERIVATIONAL SEARCH - The process of *searching back* through one's stored memories and mental representations to find the reference experience from which a current behavior or response was derived.

TRANSLATING - The process of *rephrasing* words from one type of representational system predicates to another.

UTILIZATION - A technique in which a specific strategy sequence or pattern of behavior is *paced* or *matched* in order to *influence* another's response.

VISUAL - Relating to *sight* or the sense of sight.

WELL-FORMEDNESS CONDITIONS - The set of conditions something must satisfy in order to produce an effective and ecological outcome. In NLP a particular goal is well-formed if it can be: *1) stated in positive terms. 2) defined and evaluated according to sensory based evidence. 3) initiated and maintained by the person who desires the goal. 4) made to preserve the positive by-products of the present state. 5) appropriately contextualized to fit the external ecology.*

Bibliography

Productive Thinking, Max Wertheimer, Greenwood Press, Westpoint, Connecticut, Enlarged Edition, 1959.

The Creative Process, edited by Brewster Ghiselin, Mentor Books, New American Library, New York, New York, 1952.

Out of My Later Years, Albert Einstein, The Citadel Press, Secaucus, New Jersey, 1956.

Albert Einstein, Philosopher-Scientist, Paul Arthur Schilpp, Northwestern University Press, Evanston, Ill., 1949.

Ideas and Opinions, Albert Einstein, Crown Books, New York, NY, 1954.

The World As I See It, Albert Einstein, Citadel Press, Secaucus, N.J., 1934.

Relativity, Albert Einstein, Crown Publishers, Inc., New York, NY, 1961.

EINSTEIN: A Centenary Volume, edited by A. P. French, Harvard University Press, Cambridge, Massachusetts, 1979.

Einstein For Beginners, J. Schwartz & M. McGuinness, Pantheon Books, New York, New York, 1983.

EINSTEIN: A Portrait, Pomegranate Calendars & Books, Corte Madera, CA, 1984.

ALBERT EINSTEIN, Pomegranate Calendars & Books, Corte Madera, CA, 1986.

ALBERT EINSTEIN: A Man for All Seasons, Pomegranate Calendars & Books, Corte Madera, CA, 1987.

Steps To an Ecology of Mind, Bateson, Gregory; Ballantine Books, New York, New York, 1972.

THE SECOND CYBERNETICS: Deviation-Amplifying Mutual Causal Processes, M. Maruyama, *American Scientist,* Vol. 51, pp. 164-178, 1963.

The Enfolding-Unfolding Universe: A Conversation with David Bohm, Renee Weber, *Re•Vision,* Summer/Fall 1978, pp. 24-51.

Great Inventors & Discoveries, edited by Donald Clarke, Marshall Cavendish Books Limited, London, 1978.

Encyclopedia Britannica, Encyclopedia Britannica Inc., Chicago Ill., 1979.

Ninety Nine Percent Inspiration; Mattimore, B.; American Management Association, New York, New York, 1994.

Principles of Psychology, **Britannica Great Books,** William James, Encyclopedia Britannica Inc., Chicago Ill., 1979.

Neuro-Linguistic Programming Vol. I, Dilts, R., Grinder, J., Bandler, R., DeLozier, J.; Meta Publications, Capitola, California, 1980.

The Structure of Magic Vol. I & II, Grinder, J. and Bandler, R.; Science and Behavior Books, Palo Alto, California, 1975.

Turtles All The Way Down: Prerequisites to Personal Genius, J. DeLozier & John Grinder, Grinder DeLozier & Associates, Santa Cruz, CA, 1987.

Using Your Brain, Bandler, Richard; Real People Press, Moab, Utah, 1984.

Frogs into Princes, Bandler, R. and Grinder, J.; Real People Press, Moab, Utah, 1984.

Roots of Neuro-Linguistic Programming, Dilts, R.; Meta Publications, Capitola, California, 1983.

Applications of Neuro-Linguistic Programming, Dilts, R.; Meta Publications, Capitola, California, 1983.

Changing Beliefs With NLP, Dilts, R.; Meta Publications, Capitola, California, 1990.

Beliefs; Pathways to Health and Well-Being, Dilts, R., et al; Metamorphous Press, Portland, OR, 1990.

Tools for Dreamers, Dilts, R. B., Epstein, T. & Dilts R. W.; Meta Publications, Capitola, California, 1991.

Skills for the Future, Dilts, with Bonissone, G.; Meta Publications, Capitola, California, 1993.

Strategies of Genius, Volume I, Dilts, R. B.; Meta Publications, Capitola, California, 1994.